Armoured Fighting Vehicles of the World

CHRISTOPHER F. FOSS

LONDON
IAN ALLAN LTD

First published 1971
Third edition 1977

ISBN 0 7110 0778 0

To our Parents

Published by Ian Allan Ltd., Terminal
House, Shepperton, Surrey, photoset,
printed and bound in the United Kingdom
by R. J. Acford Ltd., Industrial Estate,
Chichester, Sussex.

Contents

Abbreviations

AA	Anti-Aircraft
AFV	Armoured Fighting Vehicle
AMX	Atelier des Constructions d'Issy-les-Moulineaux
AP	Armour Piercing
APC	Armoured Personnel Carrier
APDS	Armour Piercing Discarding Sabot
APG	Aberdeen Proving Ground (United States)
APHE	Armour Piercing High Explosive
API	Armour Piercing Incendiary
APS	Armour Piercing Shot
ARV	Armoured Recovery Vehicle
ATGW	Anti-Tank Guided Weapon
AVLB	Armour Vehicle Launched Bridge
AVRE	Armoured Vehicle Royal Engineers
BAC	British Aircraft Corporation
BAOR	British Army of the Rhine
BARV	Beach Armoured Recovery Vehicle
BHP	Brake Horse Power
C & R	Command and Reconnaissance
CEV	Combat Engineer Vehicle
FCS	Fire Control System
FVRDE	Fighting Vehicles Research & Development Establishment (now the Military Vehicles and Engineering Establishment)
G /Clearance	Ground Clearance
GMC	General Motors Corporation
G /Pressure	Ground Pressure
GPO	Gun Position Officer
HE	High Explosive
HEAT	High Explosive Anti-Tank
HEI	High Explosive Incendiary
HEP	High Explosive Plastic
hp	Horse Power
HVAP	High Velocity Armour Piercing
ICBM	InterContinental Ballistic Missile
inc	Including
IR	Infra-Red
kg	Kilogramme
kg.cm^2	Kilogramme per square centimetre
km	Kilometre
km /ph	Kilometre per hour
LVT	Landing Vehicle, Tracked
max	Maximum
MBT	Main Battle Tank
MICV	Mechanised Infantry Combat Vehicle
min	Minimum
mg	Machine Gun
m	Metre
mm	Millimetre
MVEE	Military Vehicles and Engineering Establishment
NATO	North Atlantic Treaty Organisation
NBC	Nuclear, Biological, Chemical
ROF	Rate of Fire or Royal Ordnance Factory
rpm	Revolutions per minute or Rounds per minute
SPG	Self-Propelled Gun
SPH	Self-Propelled Howitzer
SPRR	Self-Propelled Recoilless Rifle
USMC	United States Marine Corps
V /Obstacle	Vertical Obstacle
W /O	With-out

Acknowledgements

The author would like to thank the following companies and individuals for their most valuable assistance during the preparation of this book.

Alvis Limited (Great Britain)
Associated Press (Great Britain)
Australian Army
Austrian Army
Belgian Army
Berliet Company (France)
Bowen-McLaughlin-York Company (USA)
Bofors Company (Sweden)
British Aircraft Corporation (Great Britain)
British Ministry of Defence (ARMY)
Bundesgrenzchutz (German Border Police)
Cadillac Gage Company (USA)
Canadian Armed Forces
Chrysler Corporation (USA)
Creusot-Loire Company (France)
DAF Company (Holland)
E.C.P. Armées (France)
Egyptian Army
Electronique Marcel Dassault (France)
EMI Limited (Great Britain)
Engesa Company (Brazil)
Euromissile (France /Germany)
FFV (Sweden)
Fiat Company (Italy)
FMC Corporation (USA)
FN (Belgium)
Finnish Army
French Army
GKN Sankey Company (Great Britain)
General Electric Company (USA)
General Motors Corporation (USA)
German Army
GIAT (France)
Hägglund and Söner (Sweden)
Hotchkiss-Brandt Company (France)
Indian Army
Irish Army
Israeli Army
Israel Aircraft Industries
Japanese Self Defence Forces
Krauss-Maffei Company (Germany)
LOHR Company (France)
Mak Maschinenbau Company (Germany)
Mercedes-Benz Company (Germany)
Mitsubishi Heavy Industries (Japan)
Messerschmitt-Bolkow-Blohm (Germany)
MOWAG Company (Switzerland)
Oto Melara Company (Italy)
Panhard and Levassor (France)
Rheinmetall Company (Germany)
Royal Armoured Corps Tank Museum (Great Britain)
Royal Danish Army
Royal Netherlands Army
SAMM Company (France)
Saviem Company (France)

Short Brothers and Harland (Great Britain)
Soltam Company (Israel)
Steyr-Daimler-Puch (Austria)
Swedish Ministry of Defence
Swiss Ministry of Defence
Technology Investments (Eire)
Thomson CSF (France)
Thyssen-Henschel (Germany)
United States Army including:
    Audio Visual Agency
    Europe
    Material Command
    Office of Chief of Information
    Tank-Automotive Command
United States Marine Corps
Vickers Limited (Great Britain)
Volvo Company (Sweden)

T. Bell (Great Britain)
R. M. Bennett (Great Britain)
S. Dunston
R. J. Icks
G. Von Rauch
J. I. Taibo
S. Tunbridge
T. Wrigley
S. Yamada

Introduction

Since the second edition of *Armoured Fighting Vehicles of the World* was published in 1975, there have been a number of significant advances in the sphere of armoured vehicles.

The new generation of Main Battle Tanks (MBTs) has at last started to make its appearance. After comparative trials between a General Motors and a Chrysler tank, the United States Army have at last selected the latter for full scale development and production and this should enter service in 1980. The Germans have developed the Leopard 2 but no date for production had been decided when this book went to press. There is also a possibility that the United States and W. Germany may well try to standardise some components of the Leopard 2 and the XM1. In Britain development of the new Chieftain for the Iranian Army is well under way and this should enter service in 1980. Due to budget restrictions the British Army will have to wait until the 1980s before it receives any new tanks with the New Chobham Armour. If the Americans and Germans do collaborate on the XM1/Leopard 2 programme, the British may well be left with no partner for their Chieftain replacement programme which, until now, has been tied up with the German programme to replace the Leopard 1 in the late 1980s. The Russians already have their new MBT in service, although there is still some doubt about the exact nature of its armament and capabilities.

The Russians were also the first to introduce a Mechanised Infantry Combat Vehicle (MICV), the BMP-1 in 1967. Since then both the Germans (with the Marder) and the French (with the AMX-10P) have introduced MICVs into their armies. The American MICV, the XM723, should enter service in 1980, but there is still no sign of the British MICV which has been under development for some time.

For many years, NATO forces have had an important edge over those of the Warsaw Pact in that the latter has not had any self-propelled artillery. The introduction of the Russian 122mm and 152mm self-propelled weapons redresses the balance. The introduction of the American Cannon Launched Guided Projectile will, however, give added capability to Allied self-propelled artillery.

In general terms, over the last few years there has been a steady increase in the armoured capabilities of the Warsaw Pact, and there is no sign that this advance will not continue in the near future. If the West is to survive it must make more strenuous efforts to standardise all its weapons not least its armour.

This book contains data, development history, variants and a list of user countries of all tanks, reconnaissance vehicles, armoured personnel carriers (and MICVs), self-propelled guns (including anti-aircraft missile systems likely to be found in the immediate battlefield area) and armoured load carriers at present in service or under development. There are many new entries and the text has been fully revised. Almost all the photographs have been replaced and most of them have not been published previously.

The author would like to thank the many governments, manufacturers and individuals from all over the world who have provided material for this book. In addition special thanks are due to Tony Cullen, Robert Forsyth (United States), John F. Milsom and Geoff Tillotson for their most valuable assistance.

January 1977   **Christopher F. Foss**

Panzerjäger K 4KH7FA, FL–12 — Austria

Armament: 1 × 105mm gun, elevation + 13°, depression − 6°
1 × 7.62mm co-axial machine gun
2 × 3 smoke dischargers
43 rounds of 105mm ammunition carried
Crew: 3
Length: 7.778m (including gun)
5.58m (excluding gun)
Width: 2.50m
Height: 2.335m (w/o cupola)
G/Clearance: .40m
Weight: 17500kg (loaded)
G/Pressure: .68kg.cm^2
Engine: Steyr Model 7FA 6 cylinder diesel 10 litres, developing 320hp at 2200rpm
Speed: 67.5km/ph (road)
Range: 520km
Fuel: 400 litres
Fording: 1.00m
V/Obstacle: .80m
Trench: 2.40m
Gradient: 75%
Armour: 8mm–40mm

Development
Development of this vehicle started in 1965 and the first prototype was completed by Saurer in 1967. It basically consists of a modified Saurer chassis on which has been fitted a French FL-12 turret with a 105mm gun, in fact the same as that fitted to AMX-13 tanks. The turret is of the oscillating type and has two magazines each holding six rounds and fires spin stabilised rounds with a m/v of 800 m/s. The modifications to the chassis have been quite extensive and include moving the engine and transmission to the rear, the drive sprocket now being at the rear, the suspension has been modified and there are now three return rollers, the APC having two.

A AEG (Austria) infra-red/white light searchlight can be fitted to the top of the turret towards the rear to assist in locating targets at night. A laser rangefinder is also mounted.

Variants
An Armoured Recovery Vehicle based on this chassis is also in service with the Austrian Army. This is known as the 4KH7FA-B

Employment
In service with the Austrian Army.

Below: *Panzerjäger K 4KH7FA*

Saurer 4K 4FA Armoured Personnel Carrier Austria

Armament: 1 × 20mm Oerlikon cannon
Crew: 2 + 8
Length: 5.40m
Width: 2.50m
Height: 2.17m (including turret)
1.65m (hull top)
G /Clearance: .42m
Weight: 13,500kg (loaded)
12,200kg (empty)
G /Pressure: .51kg.cm²
Engine: Steyr Model 4FA 6 cylinder diesel 9.981 litres, developing 250hp at 2400rpm
Speed: 65km /ph (road)
Range: 300km
Fuel: 184 litres
Fording: 1.00m
V /Obstacle: .80m
Trench: 2.20m
Gradient: 75%
Armour: 8mm–20mm

(Data relates to APC with 20mm turret.)

Development
Development of an APC was started by Saurer in 1956, the first prototype was completed in 1958 this being the 3K3H which was powered by a 3H 200hp Saurer diesel. This was followed by the 4K3H in 1959 and the 4K2P. The 4K4F was built in 1961 and the latest models are the 4K 3FA and 4K 4FA all with more powerful engines. Production has now been completed and the vehicles were built by Saurer, although Saurer was taken over by Steyr-Daimler-Puch in 1970.

Variants
There are two basic armoured personnel versions. One is armed with a 12.7mm machine gun, this being provided with front and side armour; in addition the crew can mount a total of four MG42 7.62mm machine guns on sockets around the top of the hull. The second model is fitted with an Oerlikon GAD AOA turret armed with a 20mm 204 GK gun with 100 ready rounds and a further 325 rounds in reserve. This turret can be elevated from −12° to +70°, and has armour of 15mm–35mm.
Other versions include an ambulance (Sanitätspanzer San), multiple rocket launcher with 2 × 80mm launching systems, 4K 3FA-FU (command vehicle), 4K 3FA-FU /A (artillery command vehicle), 4K 3FA-FU /FIA (anti-aircraft command vehicle), 4K 3FA-FS2 (radio vehicle), 81 mm mortar carrier (GrW1), 120mm mortar carrier (GrW 2).

Employment
Used only by the Austrian Army.

Saurer APC with 12.7mm machine gun

FN 4 RM/62F AB Armoured Car   Belgium

	Machine gun version	Gun version
Length Overall:	4.50m	5.42m
Length Hull:	4.50m	4.50m
Width:	2.26m	2.26m
Height Overall:	2.37m	2.52m
G/Clearance:	.324m	.324m
Weight loaded:	8660kg	7880kg

Data the same for both vehicles includes:
Crew: 3
Wheelbase: 2.45m
Track: 1.62m
Gradient: 60%
Armour: 6.5mm–13mm
Engine: FN 652, 6 cylinder, in-line, OHV petrol engine developing 130hp at 3500rpm
Speed: 110km/ph (road)
Range: 550/600km
Fuel: 180 litres
Fording: 1.10m

Development
This armoured car was designed by Fabrique Nationale d'Armes de Guerre of Herstal, Belgium, and uses many components of the FN 4RM Ardennes truck. The first prototype was built in 1962, followed by the second prototype in 1965. Production was completed in 1971 and 62 were built, all being delivered to the Belgian Gendarmerie.

Variants
Machine gun version: This is armed with a 60mm mortar, 2 × 7.62mm machine guns and 12 smoke dischargers. The turret has a traverse of 360°, and the machine guns can be elevated from − 10° to + 55° and the mortar from − 10° to + 75°. Ammunition carried is: 46 mortar rounds, 4830 machine gun rounds, 36 smoke grenades and 12 anti-personnel grenades.
Gun version: This is armed with a 90mm CATI gun, 1 × 7.62mm co-axial machine gun, 1 × 7.62mm anti-aircraft machine gun and 12 smoke dischargers. The turret has a traverse of 360° and the gun has an elevation from − 12° to + 27°. Ammunition carried is: 40 rounds of 90mm, 3680 machine gun rounds, 36 smoke grenades and 12 anti-personnel grenades.
Armoured Personnel Carrier: Only one of these was built. It was armed with a 7.62mm machine gun, height to hull top was 1.78m and height to cupola was 2.11m, other data was the same as for the armoured car version. Large doors were provided either side for the crew to leave the vehicle quickly.
Employment
Used only by the Belgian Gendarmerie.

FN 4 RM/62F AB Armoured Car with a 90mm gun

Cascavel EE-9 Armoured Car   Brazil

Armament: 1 x 90mm D-921 gun with an elevation of +15° and a depression of −8°
1 x 7.62mm machine gun mounted co-axially with main armament
2 x 2 smoke dischargers
20 rounds of 90mm ammunition
2400 rounds of 7.62mm ammunition
Crew: 3
Length: 5.18m (hull)
Width: 2.63m
Height: 2.36m (turret)
G/Clearance: .35m
Weight: 12,020kg (loaded) 11,420kg (empty)
Track: 2.1m
Engine: Mercedes-Benz (Brazil) Model OM 352, 6 cylinder in-line diesel developing 172hp at 2800rpm
Speed: 100km/hr
Range: 800km
Fuel: 260 litres
Fording: 1m
V/Obstacle: .6m
Gradient: 60%
Side slope: 30%
Armour: 12mm (maximum)

Development
The EE-9 was developed from June 1970 by the Engesa Company (Engenheiros Especializados SA) of Sao Paulo. The first prototype was completed in November 1970. This was armed with a turret-mounted 37mm gun. The EE-9 is now in service with the Brazilian Army who call it the CRR, or *Carro de Reconhecimento sobre Rodas*. The EE-11 armoured personnel carrier uses many automative components of the EE-9 armoured car.

The hull is of all welded steel construction of the laminate type. The driver is seated at the front, the turret is in the centre and the engine and transmission are at the rear. The rear suspension is of the Engesa developed boomerang type, this consists of a rigid axle which holds two lateral walking beams.

Production vehicles are fitted with a French built turret as mounted on the Panhard AML 90 armoured car. This is armed with a 90mm gun which fires two types of ammunition. The HE round has a m/v of 650m/s whilst the HEAT round has a m/v of 760m/s, the latter has an effective range of 1500m.

The EE-9 is not amphibious and is not provided with a NBC system. An air-conditioning system will probably be installed in those vehicles for the Qatar Army. All vehicles are provided with bullet proof tyres and powered steering.

Variants
There are no variants in service, although the vehicle could be fitted with a variety of different turrets with different armament installations.

Employment
In service with Brazil and Qatar.

Below: *The Engesa EE-9 Armoured Car*

Urutu EE-11 Armoured Personnel Carrier   Brazil

Armament: See text below
Crew: 1 + 14
Length: 6m
Width: 2.59m
Height: 2.5m (with armament)
2.25m (w/o armament)
G/Clearance: .5m
Weight: 11,800kg (loaded)
10,550kg (empty)
Track: 2.1m
Engine: Mercedes-Benz (Brazil) Model OM-352, 6 cylinder turbocharged diesel developing 165hp at 2800rpm
Speed: 90km/hr
12km/hr (water)
Range: 700km
Fuel: 250 litres
Fording: Amphibious
V/Obstacle: .6m
Trench: 1.5m
Gradient: 75%
Side Slope: 30%
Armour: 6–12mm

Development
The EE-11 was designed by Engesa (Engenheiros Especializados) of Sao Paulo with the first prototype being completed in July 1970. The first production order was received for the Brazilian Army and Marines in 1972. The Brazilian Army call the EE-9 the CTRS or *Carro de Transporte sobre Rodas Anfibo*. The EE-9 armoured car uses many automotive components of the EE-9.

The hull is of all welded steel construction and provides the crew with complete protection from small arms fire, there are firing ports in the hull sides and rear. The driver and engine are at the front of the vehicle with the personnel compartment at the rear.

The basic model is fully amphibious being propelled in the water by its wheels. The Brazilian Marines required a model with better sea-keeping capabilities and a special model for them has been developed. This is provided with four schnorkel type tubes on top of the hull and is propelled in the water by two propellers and also has electric bilge pumps.

Variants
The basic model is armed with a 7.62mm or 12.7mm machine gun on a ring mount. A wide variety of other armament installations are available including a 20mm Hägglunds turret, Commando turret with various armament including 20mm cannon or a 76mm gun, and the French turret with 90mm gun as used on the EE-9 and Panhard AML 90 armoured cars. Other engines can be installed in place of the standard Mercedes-Benz engine. Optional equipment includes a front mounted winch and night vision equipment.

Employment
In service with the Brazilian Army and Marines.

Below: *The Engesa EE-11 Armoured Personnel Carrier*

Sexton Self-Propelled Gun

Canada

Armament: 1 × 25 pounder (88mm) gun elevation + 40°, depression − 9°, traverse 25° left and 15° right
2 × Bren LMGs with 1500 rounds
25 pounder ammunition—112 cartridges, 87 HE and 18 AP projectiles
Crew: 6
Length: 6.12m
Width: 2.717m
Height: 2.870m (inc. canvas top)
2.438m (w/o canvas top)
G/Clearance: .431m
Weight: 25,855kg
G/Pressure: .81kg.cm²
Engine: Continental R975-C1 petrol engine, 400hp at 2400rpm OR
Continental R975-C4 petrol engine, 475hp at 2400rpm
Speed: 40km/ph (road)
Range: 290km (road)
Fuel: 682 litres
Fording: .914m
V/Obstacle: .609m
Trench: 1.879m
Gradient: 60%
Armour: 13mm—32mm

Development
The Sexton, full designation 25 pounder, self-propelled, tracked, Sexton, was developed in Canada. The first prototype was built late in 1942, production commenced early in 1943 at the Montreal Locomotive Works. A total of 2150 were built before production was completed late in 1945. The vehicle had an open roof although a cover was provided for use in bad weather. The Sexton served with the British Army until the 1950s.
Variants
The Sexton GPO was a Sexton without its armament and was used as a Gun Position Officer vehicle. It has additional communications equipment as well as tables and seats.
Employment
The Sexton is still used by India, Italy, Portugal and South Africa.

Above: *Sexton Self-Propelled Gun*

¾ Ton Truck 4 × 4

Canada

Armament: Crew weapons only
Crew: 8
Length: 4.749m
Width: 2.336m
Height: 2.27m
G/Clearance: .241m
Weight: 4887kg (loaded)
Engine: General Motors 6 cylinder petrol engine developing 104bhp at 3000rpm
Speed: 72km/ph (road)
Range: 713km
Fuel: 181 litres
Fording: .457m
Gradient: 60%
Armour: 8mm—12mm
Development/Variants/Employment

The ¾ ton armoured truck was designed and built in Canada during World War II. The chassis was made by General Motors of Canada and the hull by the Hamilton Bridge Company Limited. The vehicle could be used as an armoured personnel carrier, load carrier or as an ambulance. Turreted version of this vehicle was known as the Otter.

Chinese Armoured Fighting Vehicles

Type 55 Armoured Personnel Carrier: This is the Soviet BTR-40 built in China.
Type 56 Armoured Personnel Carrier: This is the Soviet BTR-152 built in China.
K-63 Armoured Personnel Carrier: This is a Chinese designed and built APC and was first seen in 1967. It has a weight of 10,000kg and is armed with a 12.7mm machine gun. It can carry ten men. Running gear is similar to that used on the T-60 light tank. Some have been delivered to Albania, Vietnam, North Korea, Tanzania.
T-60 Light Tank: This is a development of the PT-76. It has six road wheels with the driving sprocket at the rear and the idler at the front. The turret is similar in shape to the T-59. It is armed with a turret-mounted 85mm gun and a co-axial 7.mmachine gun, a 7.62mm anti-aircraft machine gun can also be fitted. It is fully amphibious being propelled in the water by waterjets. It is also used by Vietnam, Pakistan and Tanzania.

T-62 Tank: This is said to look rather like a mini-T-59 and to be armed with an 85mm gun, loaded weight is about 21,000kg, it has five large road wheels. Some have been supplied to Albania, Sudan, North Korea, Congo and Tanzania.
T-63 Tank: This is armed with an 85mm gun, it has five small road wheels and 4 support rollers.
T-59 Medium Tank: This is the Chinese copy of the Soviet T-54 tank and it has been in production since 1961. The original vehicle had no infra-red equipment, no stabiliser for the main armament and the turret only had hand traverse. Later models may have infra-red systems and improved turret traverse and stabiliser for the gun. This tank has also been exported to Albania, Vietnam, North Korea, Pakistan, Tanzania and Sudan.

Above: *T-59s of the Chinese Army*

SKOT, OT-64 Model 2A
Armoured Personnel Carrier

Czechoslovakia

Armament: 1 x 14.5mm machine gun, elevation + 29°, depression − 4°
1 x 7.62mm machine gun co-axial with 14.5mm machine gun
Crew: 2 + 18
Length: 7.44m
Width: 2.55m
Height: 2.71m (including turret)
G/Clearance: .46m
Weight: 14,300kg
Armour: 10mm
Engine: Tatra T-928-14, V-8 diesel developing 300hp at 2000rpm

Speed: 95km/ph (road)
8.9km/ph (water)
Range: 650/750km
Fording: Amphibious
V/Obstacle: .50m
Trench: 2.00m
Gradient: 60%

Development
The OT-64, also known as SKOT (Czechoslovakian designation is Středni Kolovy Obojživelny Transporter), is based on the Tatra 813 truck, development started in

1959. The 8 × 8 vehicle is fully amphibious being propelled in the water by two propellers; a trim board is erected at the front of the vehicle before entering the water. The vehicle is also fitted with a tyre pressure regulation system enabling the tyre pressures to be adjusted to suit the ground conditions. The infantry are at the rear of the vehicle and are provided with overhead hatches, rear exit doors and firing ports. The vehicle has an NBC system.

Variants

Model 1: The Polish Army has some Model 1s with a single 7.62mm machine gun in an unprotected mount. The Czechoslovakian Army Model 1s have no armament.

Model 2: This model is used by the Polish Army and has either a single 12.7mm or 7.62mm machine gun with a curved shield, this is mounted in the forward part of the vehicle.

Model 3: This model is called the Model 2A by the Czechs. It has a turret armed with a 14.5mm and a 7.62mm machine gun, the turret has a traverse of 360°, elevation + 29° and depression − 4°. The turret is situated just to the rear of the vehicle. The same turret is fitted to the Soviet BTR-60PB and BRDM-2 vehicles.

Model 4: This model has the same armament as the above but has a new turret which is higher than the Model 3, the Czechoslovakian designation of this model is the Model 2AP. The machine guns have an elevation of $+ 89\frac{1}{2}°$ and a depression of − 4°. This turret is also fitted to some late model BTR-50PKs.

Model 5: This model is a Model 1 with two Sagger anti-tank missiles mounted over the rear of the infantrymen's compartment.

Command: There are two Command models of the OT-64, these being designated the R2 and R3.

Employment: Czechoslovakia, Egypt, Hungary, India (inc Model 3s), Libya, Morocco (inc Model 3s), Poland, Sudan, Syria, Uganda (inc Model 3s).

Right: *OT-64 Model 3*

Below: *OT-64 Model 1*

OT-62, TOPAS, Model 2   Czechoslovakia

Armament: 1 × 82mm Recoilless Gun T-21 (outside of turret)
1 × 7.62mm machine gun M-59 (inside of turret)
Crew: 2 + 18
Length: 7.08m
Width: 3.14m
Height: 2.23m (inc turret)
2.038m (w/o turret)
G/Clearance: .364m
Weight: 15,000kg
G/Pressure: .53kg.cm²
Engine: Model PV-6, 6 cylinder, in-line diesel developing 300hp at 1100/1200rpm
Speed: 62km/ph (road)
11km/ph (water)
Range: 450km
Fording: Amphibious
V/Obstacle: 1.10m
Trench: 2.80m
Gradient: 70%
Armour: 10mm

Development
The OT-62 TOPAS (Transporter Obojzivelńy Pasový Stredni) is the Czechoslovakian version of the Soviet BTR-50PK APC. It is however a more powerful vehicle and the Czechs have adapted the vehicle to their own requirements. The vehicle is fully amphibious being propelled in the water by waterjets; it is also fitted with an NBC system.

Variants
Model 1: This has two projecting bays (similar to the Soviet BTR-50PU Model 2), side doors in the troop compartment and two rectangular overhead hatches. No armament is fitted although an 82mm recoilless rifle M59 may be carried and fired on the rear decking.
Model 2: This is similar to the above model but in addition has a small turret on the right bay. This is armed with a 7.62mm M59mg, a T-21 recoilless rifle can be mounted on the outside of the turret.
Model 3: This model is fitted with the same turret that is fitted to the OT-64 Model 4, it is armed with a 14.5mm and a 7.62mm machine gun, turret has a traverse of 360°. The turret is mounted over the rear troop compartment, in the centre of the vehicle. This model has a crew of 3 + 12 and a height of 2.73m. Its Czech designation is TOPAS Model 2AP. Command and ambulance versions of the OT-62 are believed to be in service.
Model 4: This has the same turret as fitted to the OT-62/OT-65 4 × 4 reconnaissance vehicles.
WPT-TOPAS: This is a special recovery vehicle developed by Poland.

Employment
In use by: Czechoslovakia, Egypt, Hungary, India, Poland, Morocco, Bulgaria, Israel, Libya, and Romania.

Above: *OT-64 Model 4 of Egyptian Army.*

OT-810 Armoured Personnel Carrier　　　Czechoslovakia

This is a Czechoslovakian copy of the World War II German Sd.Kfz.251/1 half-track. Early models of this vehicle had a petrol engine and no overhead armour. Later models had overhead armour and were powered by a Tatra 912-2 diesel. This vehicle is used both as an armoured personnel carrier and as a tractor for towing 82mm M59 recoilless guns. Some vehicles have been seen fitted with a 7.62mm M59 machine gun on the roof. The vehicle is used by Czechoslovakia and Romania.

M53/59　　　Czechoslovakia
Self-Propelled Anti-Aircraft Vehicle

Armament: 2 × 30mm M-53 cannon, elevation + 90°, depression − 10°, traverse 360°
Crew: 3
Length: 6.984m
Width: 2.41m
Height: 2.50m (w/o magazines) 3.06m (with magazines)
G/Clearance: .40m
Weight: 9500kg
Engine: Tatra T912-2 6 cylinder, in-line, water cooled diesel developing 110hp at 2200rpm
Speed: 60km/ph (road)
Range: 500km
Fording: .80m
V/Obstacle: .46m
Trench: .69m
Gradient: 60%
Armour: 10mm

Development/Variants
The M53/59 twin 30mm self-propelled anti-aircraft system is based on the Praga V3S 6 × 6 truck chassis. The guns have a vertical feed for loading whereas the towed version of these guns have a horizontal feed system. The guns have a cyclic rate of fire of 450/500 rounds per gun per minute but the practical rate of fire is 150 rounds per minute. It fires HEI or API rounds, in clips of 10 (each magazine holds 50 rounds) these have an effective anti-aircraft range of 2000m. The guns can be used both against ground and air targets.

The vehicle has a crew of three, the driver, the commander, who sits next to the driver and is provided with a transparent observation cupola on the right of the superstructure, and the gunner with the guns. There is no provision for deep wading or radar control.

Employment
In service with Czechoslovakia and Yugoslavia.

Below: *M53/59 with guns forward, the magazines for the 30mm guns can be clearly seen in this photograph*

Timoney Mk. 3 Armoured Personnel Carrier   Eire

Armament: twin 7.62mm machine guns
Crew: 1 + 11
Length: 4.95m
Width: 2.406m
Height: 2.475m (turret)
2.032m (hull top)
G/Clearance: .381m
Weight: 8164kg (loaded)
6350kg (empty)
Engine: Chrysler Type 360 CID, 8 cylinder water-cooled petrol developing 200 bhp at 4000rpm
Speed: 98km/hr (road)
4.8km/hr (water)
Range: 483km
Fuel: 273 litres
Fording: Amphibious
V/Obstacle: .762m
Gradient: 60%
Armour: 10mm

Development

In 1972, Technology Investments Limited started the development of an armoured personnel carrier. The first prototype was completed in 1973 with the further two prototypes following in 1974/75. The Timoney has been designed to meet the requirements of the Irish Army for employment in Ireland, and, as a part of United Nations Forces, in any part of the world. So far armoured personnel carriers Mks. 1, 2 and 4 have been developed.
It has a hull of all welded construction with the driver at the front and the engine, which is the same as that used in the M113 APC, to the rear of the driver. Prototypes are armed with a manually operated turret with twin 7.62mm machine guns; other armament installations are being designed. The Timoney is fully amphibious being propelled in the water by its wheels. Its steering is power assisted and bullet proof tyres are fitted as standard. The basic vehicle can be adopted for use as a command vehicle, cargo carrier or ambulance.

Variants

An Armoured Reconnaissance Vehicle called the Mk. 2 has been developed, this is armed with a turret mounted 76mm gun, a 4 × 4 Amphibious load carrier is also being developed. According to the manufacturers it is possible to design a 6 × 6 APC using the same automotive components as the 4 × 4 model.

Employment

Trials. Not yet in production.

Below: *The Timoney Mk. 3 Armoured Personnel Carrier*

AMX-30 Main Battle Tank

Armament: 1 × 105mm gun, elevation + 20° depression − 8°
1 × 12.7mm mg or 20mm cannon co-axial with main armament, it can however be elevated to + 40°
1 × 7.62mm machine gun on commander's cupola
2 × 2 smoke grenade launchers
50 rounds of 105mm ammunition, 600 rounds of 12.7mm ammunition, 1600 rounds of 7.62mm ammunition
Crew: 4
Length: 9.48m (gun forward)
6.59m (hull only)
Width: 3.10m
Height: 2.85m (top of cupola)
2.28m (turret roof)
G /Clearance: .44m
Weight: 36,000kg (loaded)
G /Pressure: .77kg.cm²
Engine: Hispano-Suiza HS-110, 12 cylinder multi-fuel, water cooled engine developing 700hp at 2400rpm. Engine is built in France by Saviem.
Speed: 65km /ph (road)
Range: 650km (road)
Fuel: 970 litres
Fording: 2.00m
4.00m (with schnorkel)
V /Obstacle: .93m
Trench: 2.90m
Gradient: 60%

Development

In 1956, France, Germany and Italy decided to build a common tank. This idea did not work out and France decided to build the AMX-30. The first prototype AMX-30 was completed in 1960, this being followed by the second prototype in 1961. These were followed by a further seven models in 1963 and pre-production tanks in 1965. In 1966 the tank entered production and the first French M-47 units were re-equipped with AMX-30s in the summer of 1967.
The vehicle is fitted with infra-red driving and fighting equipment, it also has an NBC system and can be fitted with a schnorkel. Under development is a laser rangefinder. The 105mm gun can fire either hollow charge rounds (m/v 1000 m/s) or HE rounds (m/v 700 m/s), maximum rate of fire is 8rpm. A 120mm Smooth Bore gun is reported to be under development for the AMX-30.

Variants

AMX-30 Export Model: This has no NBC system, no schnorkel or infra-red equipment and a simple cupola.
AMX-30S: This model been developed for use in hot climates; it is fitted with sandshields and its engine develops only 620hp at 2400rpm; the gearbox has been modified. It can be fitted with air conditioning.
AMX-30 SHAHINE: This has a total of six Crotale missiles in the ready to launch position and has been ordered by Saudi-Arabia.
AMX-30 Anti-Aircraft Tank: This is simply an AMX-30 chassis with the turret of the AMX-13 A/A tank. It is armed with 2 × 30mm guns. It is in production for Saudi-Arabia.
AMX-30 155mm GCT: This 155mm self-propelled gun is at present under test. For full details see separate entry.
AMX-30 ACRA: An AMX-30 tank was used to test the 142mm ACRA anti-tank system. In 1973 however the ACRA system was cancelled.
AMX-30 Recovery Tank: This is designed to carry out repairs in the field and to carry out this role it is fitted with a crane (can lift 13/20,000kg), main winch (35,000kg with 120m of cable), auxiliary winch (4000kg and 120m of cable) and a dozer blade at the front. It is armed with a 7.62mm machine gun and smoke dischargers. In production and service.
An improved model is the AMX-30 DI.
AMX-30 Bridgelayer Tank: This tank can lay a class 50 bridge across a 20m ditch. The bridge is 22m long, 3.15m wide (w/o widening panels) and 3.95m wide (with widening panels), when laid out. It is entering service.
AMX-30 Roland Anti-Aircraft Tank: This is now in production and has two Roland missiles in the ready to fire position, with a further eight in reserve. It is a complete weapons system having its own radar.
Pluton Weapon System: This is an AMX-30 chassis fitted with a Pluton

	155mm SPG	ARV	Bridgelayer	Roland
Length Overall:	10.40m	7.18m	11.40m	6.65m
Width Overall:	3.115m	3.14m	3.95m	3.10m
Height Overall:	3.30m	2.65m	4.29m	3.02m
Weight Loaded:	41,000kg	40,000kg	42,500kg	33,000kg
Crew:	4	4	3	3

tactical nuclear missile with a range of over 100km.

AMX-30 Training Tank: This is an AMX-30 on which the turret has been replaced by an observation cupola.

AMX-30 with TSE 6000 Javelot: This is a close-air defence system under development by Thomson-CSF.

AMX-30 with RAPACE radar: An AMX-30 has been fitted with the EMD Rapace tank detection radar for trials purposes.

Employment

The AMX-30 is used by Chile, France, Greece (and ARV), Iraq, Libya, Peru, Saudi-Arabia, Spain, Qatar, Morocco, and Venezuela. This includes those on order.

AMX-30 fitted with a Schnorkel for deep fording

AMX-30 Main Battle Tanks of Greek Army

The AMX-30 Anti-Aircraft Tank

19

The AMX-30 Armoured
Recovery Vehicle

The AMX-30 Bridgelayer
Tank in the travelling
position

The AMX-30 fitted with
the Roland Anti-Aircraft
System

AMX-13 Light Tank   France

Armament: 1 × 90 mm gun, elevation + 12½°, depression − 5½°
1 × 7.62mm machine gun co-axial with main armament
1 × 7.62mm machine gun on commander's cupola (optional)
2 × 2 smoke dischargers. (Some AMX-13s have 7.5mm mgs.)
34 rounds of 90mm and 3600 rounds of 7.62mm ammunition
Crew: 3
Length: 6.36m (with gun)
4.88m (w/o gun)
Width: 2.50m
Height: 2.30m (cupola)
G/Clearance: .37m
Weight: 15,000kg (loaded)
13,000kg (empty)
G/Pressure: .76kg.cm²
Engine: SOFAM 8GXb 8 cylinder water cooled, 8.25 litres petrol engine developing 270hp at 3200rpm (built by Saviem)
Speed: 60km/ph (road)
Range: 350km/400km (road)
Fuel: 480 litres
Fording: .60m
V/Obstacle: .65m
Trench: 1.60m
Gradient: 60%
Armour: 10mm 40mm

Note. *The data relates to the AMX-13 with the new 90mm gun.*

Development
The design of the AMX-13 started shortly after the end of World War II. AMX standing for the design centre (Atelier des Constructions d'Issy-les-Moulineaux) and

13 for the original requested weight. The first prototype was built in 1949 and deliveries to the French Army started in 1952. The AMX-13 tank chassis has been used for a whole range of AFVs, a few of which are described below, the rest later in the book. The AMX-13 has been constantly modified to keep it an effective weapon.

Variants
AMX-13 Model 51: This was the first model to enter service. It was armed with a 75mm gun in an FL-10 turret. It was armed with a 75mm gun and a 7.5mm or 7.62mm machine gun and four smoke dischargers. 37 rounds of 75mm ammunition are carried, of these 12 rounds were in two revolver type magazines with 6 rounds each. This enabled the tank to fire 12 rounds very quickly. The drawback being that these magazines then had to be re-loaded again from outside of the vehicle.

AMX-13 with FL-11 turret: This was designed in the mid-1950s for use in Algeria. It is armed with a short 75mm gun in an FL-11 turret.

AMX-13 Model 58 with FL-12 turret: This is armed with a 105mm gun that fires fin-stabilised, non-rotating hollow charge rounds. These rounds have a m/v of 800 m/s and will penetrate 360mm of armour. 32 rounds of 105mm ammunition are carried.

AMX-13 with 90mm gun: This is the latest model of the AMX-13. The barrel

Below: *AMX-13 Bridgelayer*

21

is a 75mm barrel which has been rebored and an insulating jacket fitted. The gun fires 90mm hollow charge rounds with a m/v of 950 m/s and will penetrate 320mm of armour; 34 rounds of ammunition are carried.

AMX-13 Model 51 with SS-11 missiles: This retains its gun armament but also has four SS-11 ATGW, these are mounted two either side of the gun. The missiles have an effective range of 3000m. This system is in service with the French Army. A later version, still under test, is fitted with the TCA optical/infra-red guidance system for the missiles, a similar guidance system is fitted to the AMX-13 with HOT.

AMX-13 with HOT ATGW: This version was developed to prototype stage but has not been adopted by French Army.

AMX Armoured Recovery Vehicle (Char de Dépannage Model 55): This has spades at the rear, 15 ton capacity winch, an auxiliary winch, 5 ton "A" frame, lighting equipment and tools. The French ARVs are armed with a 7.5 or 7.62mm mg, the Netherlands ARVs have six smoke dischargers and a 7.62mm mg. Basic data is similar to the AMX-13 except:
Crew: 3
Width: 2.60m
Length: 5.515m
Weight: 15,000kg
Height: 2.682m

AMX-13 Bridgelayer: Called Poseur de Pont by the French. It is a modified AMX-13 chassis fitted with a scissors bridge.

When opened out this is 7.15m in length and can take tanks up to class 25, two of these bridges used together can take class 50 tanks. Basic data is similar to the AMX-13 except:
Weight: 19,700kg (with bridge)
Length: 7.75m (with bridge)
Width: 3.05m
Height: 4.30m (with bridge)

AMX-13 Training Tank: This is an AMX tank without its turret and used for driver training. The French also have some vehicles with M-24 Chaffe turrets.

Employment
Used by Algeria, Argentina (including bridge-layers), Cambodia, Chile, Dominican Republic, Ecuador, Egypt, France, India, Indonesia, Ivory Coast, Kenya, Lebanon, Morocco, Netherlands (including ARV), Nepal (from Israel), Peru, Saudi-Arabia, Singapore (from Israel), Switzerland (called Pz-51), Tunisia, Venezuela, Guatemala, and El Salvador. Argentina has assembled AMX-13s, the first one being completed late in 1969.

AMX-13 with 105mm Gun of Dutch Army

AMX-10RC
Armoured Reconnaissance Vehicle

Armament: 1 × 105mm gun
1 × 7.62mm machine gun co-axial with main armament
2 × 2 smoke dischargers
Crew: 4
Length: 6.243m (hull)
Width: 2.84m
Height: 2.565m (overall)
G/Clearance: .3m (adjustable)
Weight: 15,000kg (loaded)
Track: 2.425m
Engine: Hispano-Suiza HS-115 eight cylinder supercharged diesel developing 280hp at 3000rpm
Speed: 85km/hr
7km/hr (water)
Range: 800km
Fording: Amphibious
V/Obstacle: .7m
Trench: 1.6m
Gradient: 60%

Development

The AMX-10RC uses many components of the tracked AMX-10P MICV. The first prototype was shown to the public in 1973 and in 1975 it was announced that the AMX-10RC would enter production in 1977/78 and would replace the Panhard EBR 8 × 8 armoured car by the early 1980s.

The 105mm gun has an elevation of +20° and a depression of −8°, traverse being a full 360°. It fires a fin-stabilised HEAT-T round with a m/v of 1090m/s or a HE round with a m/v of 800m/s. The fire control system includes a laser rangefinder and a passive night TV system, the latter having been developed by Thomson-CSF especially for the vehicle.

The vehicle is fully amphibious being propelled in the water by two water jets, one each side of the hull. A NBC system is also provided as is a passive night periscope for the driver. The AMX-10RC is fitted with a hydropneumatic suspension system which allows the driver to adjust the ground clearance to suit the type of ground being crossed.

Variants

A prototype of a 6 × 6 wheeled APC called the AMX-10R was shown in 1971 but this has not been put into production. A tracked version of the AMX-10RC has also been built, this is called the AMX-10C, and weighs 14,500kg. This could well be the replacement for the AMX-13 Light tank.

Employment

In production for the French Army.

Below: *The AMX-10RC 6 × 6 reconnaissance vehicle*

EBR 75 Heavy Armoured Car   France

Armament: See below
Length: 7.33m (o/a FL-10 turret)
6.15m (o/a FL-11 turret)
5.56m (vehicle only)
Width: 2.42m
Height: 2.32m (FL-11 on 8 wheels)
2.24m (FL-11 on 4 wheels)
G/Clearance: .41m (on 8 wheels)
.33m (on 4 wheels)
Weight: 15,200kg (loaded FL-10)
13,500kg (loaded FL-11)
G/Pressure: .75kg.cm² (on 8 wheels)
Engine: Panhard 12 cylinder petrol engine, developing 200hp at 3700rpm.
Crew: 4
Speed: 105km/ph (road)
Range: 650km
Fuel: 380 litres
Fording: 1.20m
V/Obstacle: .40m
Trench: 2.00m
Gradient: 60% +
Armour: 10mm–40mm

Development

In 1937 Panhard started to design an 8 × 8 armoured car for the French Army. A prototype was completed in December 1939 and the vehicle was given the Panhard No. Model 201. The vehicle, together with its drawings, were lost during the war. Development work started again after the war and the first post-war prototype was completed in July 1948. This had an FL-11 turret and was called the EBR 75 (Engin Blindé Reconnaissance), its Panhard designation being Model 212. The vehicle entered production in August 1950 and production was completed in 1960 by which time 1200 had been built. The EBR has a number of unusual features. It has a crew of four which consists of a commander, gunner and two drivers (one at the front and one at the rear). All eight wheels are powered and when crossing rough country its centre four wheels, which have steel treads, can

be lowered into position. All of the turrets used, the FL-10 and FL-11, are of the oscillating type.

Variants

EBR 75 with FL-11 turret: Also known as type B, has a 75mm gun, elevation + 15°, depression − 10°, with 56 rounds of ammunition. This was the first model to enter service. Other data see below.

EBR 75 with FL 10 turret: this has a 75mm gun with an elevation of + 13° and a depression of − 6°. A total of 38 rounds of ammunition are carried. The gun has automatic loading, ie two revolving type magazines hold six rounds each. Three 7.5mm mgs are fitted, one co-axial with the main gun and one fixed for the use of each driver. Two smoke dischargers are fitted either side of the turret. It is also known as the Model A.

EBR 75 with 90mm gun in FL-11 turret: This is the latest version and mounts a 90mm gun that fires fin-stabilised ammunition, all earlier versions will be refitted with this new gun. It is also called Model C.

EBR Anti-Aircraft Vehicle: One of these was built in 1952. It consisted of an EBR chassis on which was mounted a turret armed with 2 × 30mm cannon.

EBR ETT Armoured Personnel Carrier: This had the Panhard No. Model 238, the first vehicle was built in 1957 and a total of 30 were built. There were two models—one had a single large mg turret and the other had two small turrets, one at each end of the vehicle. Some vehicles had their metal centre wheels replaced by conventional wheels with tyres. This is used by Portugal.

Employment

Used by France, Mauritania, Morocco and Portugal.

Above: *EBR 75 with FL-11 turret mounting a 90mm gun*

Panhard AML Light Armoured Car — France

Armament: 1 × 60mm mortar, elevation + 76°, depression − 15°
1 × 12.7mm machine gun, elevation + 75°, depression − 11°
41 rounds of 60mm mortar ammunition
1200 rounds of 12.7mm machine gun ammunition
Crew: 3
Length: 3.79m
Width: 1.97m
Height: 2.12m (over searchlight)
1.885m (turret top)
G /Clearance: .33m
Weight: 4800kg (loaded)
Track: 1.62m
Wheelbase: 2.50m
Engine: Panhard Model 4 HD, 4 cylinder air-cooled petrol engine developing 90hp at 4700rpm
Speed: 100km /ph (road)
Range: 600km (road)
Fuel: 156 litres
Fording: 1.10m
V /Obstacle: .30m
Trench: .80m (one channel)
3.10m (four channels)
Gradient: 60%
Armour: 8mm−12mm

Note. *The above data relates to the AML with the HE 60-12 turret.*

Development
The AML-245 is manufactured by Panhard in Paris. The first prototype was completed in 1959 followed by the first production vehicle in 1961. Since then the vehicle has been built in large numbers and exported all over the world, in addition a production line has been established in South Africa, this, however, is not run by Panhard. AML means Automitrailleuse Légère, or light armoured car. The AML can be fitted with a variety of night fighting and night driving equipment and is airportable by aircraft and helicopters (ie the SA 321 Super Frelon). The AML has been continuously developed over the last 10 years and a full list of variants is listed below. Many components of the AML are used in the Panhard M-3, which is described later in the book.

Variants
AML with HE 60-7 turret (also known as Model A): This is armed with a 60mm mortar (Model CS DTAT or Hotchkiss Brandt CM 60A1) with an elevation of + 76°, depression − 15°, this has a range of 300m−1700m and 2 × 7.62mm machine guns. These have an elevation of + 60° and a depression of − 15°. 53 rounds of 60mm and 3800 rounds of 7.62mm ammunition are carried. Four ENTAC missiles can be fitted as required, this then becomes the Model D.
AML with HE 60-20 turret (also known as Model E): This is armed with a 60mm breach-loaded mortar with an elevation of + 76° and a depression of − 15° and a 20mm M621 cannon. This has an elevation of + 50° and a depression of − 8°. 39 rounds of 60mm and 300 rounds of 20mm ammunition are carried. A 7.62mm anti-aircraft machine gun is fitted to the roof of the vehicle and 1000 rounds of 7.62mm ammunition are carried.

The AML with H-90 turret mounted 90mm gun

AML with H-90 turret (also known as Model C): This is armed with a 90mm gun with an elevation of +15° and a depression of −8° and a co-axial 7.62mm machine gun. The 90mm gun has an effective range of 1500m when firing HE rounds (m/v 650 m/s) or 2400m when firing fin-stabilised hollow charge rounds (m/v 760 m/s). Twenty rounds of 90mm and 2400 rounds of 7.62mm ammunition are carried. In addition there are two smoke dischargers either side of the turret. If required 2 ENTAC or SS-11 ATGW can be mounted either side of the 90mm gun.

AML-30: This has a new turret mounting a 30mm HS 831A cannon and a co-axial 7.62mm machine gun. A 7.62mm anti-aircraft machine gun is mounted on the turret roof. There are two smoke dischargers mounted either side of the turret. 200 rounds of 30mm and 2200 rounds of 7.62mm ammunition are carried.

AML with NA 2 turret: This was an experimental vehicle and was a basic AML fitted with a NA 2 turret mounting 4 SS-11 ATGW (+2 reserve) or 2 SS-12 (+2 reserve) ATGW. Also fitted were 2 ACL 89mm anti-tank rockets or 2 × 7.62mm machine guns.

AML S 530 anti-aircraft vehicle: The prototype was completed in 1969 and the first production vehicle in 1971. It is a basic AML, fitted with a new turret designed by SAMM (Société d'Applications des Machines Motrices). This mounts 2 × 20mm 621 automatic cannon, with powered traverse and elevation from +75° to −10°, traverse being 360°. Effective range is 1300m and rate of fire is 740rpm per barrel. 600 rounds of 20mm ammunition are carried. In addition there are two smoke dischargers either side of the turret.

Amphibious kit

An amphibious kit has been developed that can be fitted to any of the AML series. This kit consists of thin steel sheets around the hull of the vehicle, these are filled with a self-extinguishable non-spongy synthetic matter. A propeller kit is available, this gives the vehicle a speed of 6−7km/ph in the water. Loaded weight of an AML 90 with the amphibious kit is 5750kg.

Employment

The AML is used by Algeria, Burundi, Cambodia, Congo, Ecuador, Eire, Ethiopia, France, Iraq, Israel, Ivory Coast, Kenya, Libya, Mauritania, Morocco, Malaysia, Nigeria, Portugal, Rhodesia (from South Africa), Rwanda, Saudi-Arabia, Senegal, South Africa (known as the Eland), Spain, Tunisia, Abu Dhabi, Chad, Upper Volta, Lebanon, Venezuela, and Zaire.

The AML-30 with a 30mm HS 831A cannon

The AML with an HE 60-7 turret

The AML S 530 Anti-Aircraft Vehicle with twin 20mm cannon

The AML with the HE 60-20 turret

LOHR VP 90 Lightweight Fighting Vehicle   France

Armament: See below
Crew: 1 + 3
Length: 3.6m
Width: 1.85m
Height: 1.05m (w/o armament)
G/Clearance: .31m
Weight: 2700kg (loaded)
2100kg (empty)
G/Pressure: .268kg/cm
Engine: Citroen Model CX 2200 four cylinder petrol engine developing 102hp at 5500rpm.
Speed: 90km/hr
Range: 400km
Gradient: 70%
Side Slope: 60%

Development/Variants

The Lohr Company of Hangenbieten is the most recent company to market the VP 90 tracked vehicle, they have purchased the manufacturing and marketing rights from Hotchkiss-Brandt who no longer build armoured vehicles.

The VP 90 is only armoured on the front part of the hull and has an open roof. It relies on its small size and speed for survival. The basic VP 90 can be adapted for a variety of roles including ambulance, command, reconnaissance, anti-tank, mortar towing vehicle (ie 120mm Brandt Mortar), supply vehicle (one man plus 600kg of supplies) and personnel carrier (driver and four men).

It can be fitted with a variety of armament installations including a Milan missile launcher and four missiles (or a TOW or Dragon missile system), 60mm breech loaded mortar and a machine gun, one or two 20mm cannon, various combinations of 7.62mm and 12.7mm machine guns, SS-11 ATGW system and various reciolless rifles.

The vehicle can be carried under helicopters such as the SA330 Super Frelon. The vehicle also has an electrical positive and negative nose-lift device which enables the nose to be elevated to +9° and its tail to be elevated to +4°.

Employment

Trials: not yet in service.

Below: *The LOHR VP 90 tracked vehicle with Milan ATGW*

AMX-10P Family France
Mechanised Infantry Combat Vehicle

Armament: 1 × 20mm cannon M-693 and 1 × 7.62mm machine gun in a mount with a traverse of 360°, elevation + 50° and depression − 8°. 800 rounds of 20mm ammunition (of which 350 are ready for use) and 2000 rounds of 7.62mm ammunition (of which 900 are ready for use) are carried.
4 smoke grenade launchers mounted on the rear of the vehicle.
Crew: 2 + 9
Length: 5.778m
Width: 2.780m
Height: 2.54m (overall)
1.87m (hull top)
G/Clearance: 0.45m
Weight: 13,800kg (loaded)
11,300kg (empty)
Engine: Hispano-Suiza HS 115-2, V-8 watercooled engine developing 276hp at 3000rpm.
8.21 litres
Speed: 65km/ph (road)
7.92km/ph (water)
Range: 600km
Fording: Amphibious
V/Obstacle: 0.70m
Trench: 1.60m
Gradient: 60%
G/Pressure: .53kg.cm²

Development
The prototype was called the AMX-10A and was shown at the 1969 French Satory exhibition. The first vehicle in the series is the AMX-10P, from this has been developed a whole new range of armoured fighting vehicles for the French Army, both tracked and wheeled. The vehicles are fully amphibious being propelled in the water by water jets, they are fitted with NBC systems and/or infrared/image intensifier driving and fighting equipment.

Variants—Tracked
AMX-10P: This is now in production. It is an infantry combat vehicle and has started to replace the AMX Model 56 APC. It carries nine infantrymen and these are provided with overhead hatches, periscopes and firing ports in the rear. Under development is a version with Milan ATGW, also being developed is a stabilisation system for the gun turret.
AMX-10TM: This version is also in production and tows the Hotchkiss-Brandt 120mm mortar, the vehicle has a crew of six and carries 60 mortar rounds.
AMX-10PC: This is a command vehicle and is in production. It has a crew of six. the vehicle has been provided with an additional generator. Additional working space can be provided by erecting awnings at the rear and side of the vehicle.

Below: *AMX-10PC Command Vehicle*

AMX-10P (Ratac): This is the standard armoured personnel carrier with the turret removed and replaced by the RATAC (Fire Radar for Field Artillery), this version is now in service with the French Army.

AMX-10P (HOT): This has its turret replaced by a new turret with a total of four HOT missiles in the ready to launch position, a further 15 missiles are carried inside the hull. A 7.62mm machine gun with 2000 rounds of ammunition is also mounted in the turret. Crew is five men.

AMX-10P (Training): This has its turret removed and replaced by an observation cupola for the instructor and another trainee driver.

AMX-10P (Ambulance): This is a standard AMX-10P with armament removed and can carry a maximum of ten casualties.

AMX-10 ECH (Repair): This was known as the AMX-10D and has a crew of five men. It has a Toucan turret which is armed with a 20mm cannon and a co-axial 7.62mm machine gun, the turret has manual traverse rather than powered traverse as has the standard AMX-10P.

AMX-10C: For details of this family the reader is referred to the entry on the AMX-10RC 6 × 6 vehicle.

AMX-10P (ACRA): This project has been cancelled.

Further improvements to the AMX-10P: The French Army is considering the following improvements to the AMX-10P:
(1)   Adding the Milan ATGW system
(2)   Installation of a new transmission
(3)   Stabilisation system for the 20mm gun turret

Employment
The AMX-10P is in service with France, Greece, Saudi-Arabia, and Qatar.

Below: *AMX-10TM with 120mm mortar*

Bottom: *AMX-10P with HOT Missile Installation*

AMX VCI   France
Armoured Personnel Carrier/Infantry Combat Vehicle

Armament: 1 x 7.5mm or 7.62mm or 12.7mm machine gun
Crew: 1 + 12
Length: 5.544m
Width: 2.51m
Height: 2.32m (with turret)
1.92m (w/o turret)
G/Clearance: .48m
Weight: 14,000kg (loaded)
11,700kg (empty)
G/Pressure: .70kg.cm^2
Engine: SOFAM 8 GXb 8 cylinder petrol engine developing 250hp at 3200rpm
Speed: 65km/ph (road)
Range: 350/400km (road)
Fuel: 410 litres
Fording: .60m
V/Obstacle: .65m
Trench: 1.60m
Gradient: 60%
Armour: 10mm–30mm

Note. *Above dimensions can vary according to date built.*

Development/Variants

The specification for the AMX APC was issued in 1954 and production commenced in 1956. It is based on the AMX tank chassis which has been lengthened and vehicles can be seen with three or four return rollers. It was originally called the AMX-VTP (Véhicule Transport de Personnel) or TT.CH.Mle.56.(Transport de Troupe Chenillé Model 56) but it is now referred to as the AMX VCI (Véhicule de Combat d'Infanterie). The machine gun can be mounted in a turret (7.5mm or 7.62mm) or on a ring mount (12.7mm mg). It can also be fitted with a turret mounted 20mm cannon. The infantry carried can fire their weapons through firing ports in the sides and rear of the vehicle. The vehicle has an NBC system and can be fitted with infra-red driving lights. A number of these vehicles were built in Belgium. The vehicle has no amphibious capability.
Command Vehicle: This is known as the 'Véhicule de Commandement', and has been fitted with additional radios, map boards and so on. It has a crew of 4–9 men and is recognisable by its three radio aerials.
Ambulance: Known as the 'Véhicule Sanitaire Model 56', no armament is fitted. It has a crew of four and can carry four seated and three stretcher patients. Basic data is similar to the APC except that its loaded weight is 13,500kg.

Above: *Netherlands Army AMX VCI. Note the six smoke dischargers*

Dozer Vehicle: This is simply an AMX APC with a dozer blade fitted at the front, known as the 'Char AMX Dozer'. Loaded weight is 16,200kg.

Battery Command Vehicle: This has been developed for use with artillery, for example the 155mm SPG. Equipment fitted includes additional radios, map boards and fire control equipment. Under development is an electronic fire control computer. Data similar to the APC except for its crew of seven.

Mortar Vehicles: These are called AMX-VCPM (Véhicule Chenillé Porte-Mortier) and there are two versions:

81mm mortar with elevation of +43° to +80°, traverse 40°, 128 rounds carried, crew of 6. Mortar can also be fired away from the vehicle

120mm mortar with an elevation of +45° to +77°, traverse 46°, 60 rounds carried, crew of five. Mortar can also be fired away from the vehicle.

Pioneer Vehicle: Known as the AMX-VCG (Véhicule de Combat du Génue). This is fitted with a dozer blade, winch. 'A' frame, search-light and other equipment. It has a crew of 10, armed with a 12.7mm mg, weight 17,800kg, length 6.37m and height 3.46m.

Cargo Vehicle: When used as a cargo vehicle the AMX VCI can carry 3,170kg of cargo.

Missile Launcher Vehicle: This is a standard AMX VCI fitted with two missile launchers at the rear, each launcher having two missiles. A total of 26 ENTAC missiles are carried and it has a crew of five. Another version has two SS-11 missiles, one either side of the commander's cupola.

Artillery Support Vehicle: This is used to support the AMX 155mm SPG. It has a crew of eight and carries 25 shells, 25 cartridge bags and 24 fuses. It can also tow an ammunition trailer. Loaded weight is 13,700kg.

Roland Anti-Aircraft Missile Vehicle: This was a trials vehicle and mounted 2 Roland SAMs in the ready to fire position.

TOW Launcher Vehicle: DAF have fitted an AMX VCI of the Netherlands Army with a launcher system for the American TOW ATGW.

Employment

Used by Argentina, Belgium, France, Italy, The Netherlands. Abu Dhabi, Ecuador, Indonesia, and Venezuela.

Right: *AMX APC of Dutch Army with TOW missile installation*

Below: *AMX-VCG fitted with its Dozer Blade and 'A' frame*

Panhard M-3 Armoured Personnel Carrier   France

Armament: See below, according to requirements
Crew: 2 + 10
Length: 4.457m
Width: 2.40m
Height: 2.48m (turret)
2.0m (w /o turret)
G /Clearance: .35m
Weight: 6100kg (loaded)
Track: 2.05m
Wheelbase: 2,70m
Engine: Panhard Model 4 HD, 4 cylinder, air cooled petrol engine developing 90hp at 4700rpm
Speed: 100km /ph (road)
4km /ph (water)
Range: 600km (road)
Fuel: 165 litres
Fording: Amphibious
V /Obstacle: .30m
Trench: .80m (with 1 channel)
Gradient: 60%
Armour: 8mm-12mm

Development
The Panhard M-3 armoured personnel carrier is based on components of the AML family, 95% of the components of the M-3 are interchangeable with those of the AML. The prototype M-3 was built in 1969 and the first production model in 1971. The prototype was rather square in appearance. In recent years the vehicle has been sold in large numbers all over the world. The hull of the M-3 is of all welded construction. There are doors on either side of the vehicle and twin doors at the rear. A circular opening in the front part of the roof can be fitted with a variety of turrets or mounts. There is also a hatch on the rear part of the roof allowing use of a machine gun mounted on a rail. There are flaps in the sides of the vehicle and firing ports in the rear door. The M-3 is fully amphibious without preparation; it is propelled in the water by its wheels.

Variants
The basic vehicle can be used as an armoured personnel carrier, load carrier, ambulance (VTS), riot control vehicle, mortar carrier, repair vehicle (VAT), command post (VPC), radio vehicle or missile vehicle. A wide range of armament can be fitted, some of which is listed below:
Turret TL.2.80 with twin 7.62mm machine guns.
Turret MAS T.20.13.621 with AME 621 20mm cannon.
Turret TL 52 S with one 7.62mm machine gun and 1 Strim rocket launcher.
Turret TL 52 3S with one 7.62mm machine gun and 3 Strim rocket launchers.
Mount CB.20 M621 with 20mm cannon.
Mount CB.60.HB with 60mm mortar.

Above: *Panhard M-3 with single 7.62mm machine gun*

Mount CB.127 with 12.7mm machine gun.
Mount CB.80 and CB.52 with 7.62mm machine gun.
Mount STB.80 STB.52, STB.MG with 7.62mm machine gun.
Mount STB.80, STR.52 and STR.B with 7.62mm machine gun.

Panhard M-3 VDA: This was shown for the first time at Satory in June 1973. It has been designed by Panhard in association with EMD, CNMP, Galileo and Oerlikon. It is basically an M-3 chassis with a turret mounting 2 × 20mm HS 820 SL guns with an elevation of + 85° and a depression of − 5°, these have power traverse and elevation. A total of 650 rounds of 20mm ammunition are carried.

In addition there is a 7.62mm machine gun on the roof of the vehicle. It has a crew of three men. There are two stabilisers either side of the hull, which can be let down to provide a stable firing platform. The vehicle is fitted with a radar scanner and a computor sight.

Employment
Used by Abu-Dhabi, Congo, Iraq, Eire, Kenya, Lebanon, Malaysia, Saudi-Arabia, Angola, France, Portugal, and Spain.

Panhard M-3 HOT: This has a turret with four HOT missiles in the ready to launch position with a further 10 missiles in reserve.

Panhard M-3 VPM: This is armed with an 81mm mortar, a total of 60 mortar bombs are carried.

A Panhard M-3 with HOT ATGW missile installation

Panhard M-3 VDA Anti-Aircraft Vehicle

A Panhard M-3 with 60mm Hotchkiss-Brandt mortar

Berliet VXB 170 Multi-Role Vehicle France

Armament: See below
Crew: 1 + 11
Length: 5.99m
Width: 2.50m
Height: 2.05m (w/o turret)
G/Clearance: .45m (transfer box)
Weight: 12,700kg (loaded)
9800kg (empty)
Engine: Berliet V8 diesel, 6.92 litres, developing 170hp at 3000rpm
Speed: 85km/ph (road)
4km/ph (water)
Range: 750km
Fuel: 220 litres
Fording: Amphibious
Trench: nil

Gradient: 60%
Armour: 7mm (maximum)

Development

This vehicle was originally known as the Berliet BL 12. The first of two prototypes was built in March 1968. One of these was tested by the French Army in 1969 and the other retained by Berliet. The first of five VXBs was built in May 1971 and tested by the French Gendarmerie. In 1973 a production order was given to

Below: *A Berliet VXB with 7.62mm machine gun*

Berliet for 50 vehicles for the French Gendarmerie; production commenced in 1973 at the Berliet factory at Bourg.

The VXB is a 4 × 4 vehicle and its hull is of all-welded construction. Firing ports are provided in the hull and the crew can enter and leave the vehicle by way of side, rear and roof hatches. It is fully amphibious being propelled in the water by its wheels. A 3500/4500kg winch is fitted at the front. Optional extras are many and include heater, radios, NBC system, night driving equipment and a dozer blade.

Variants

The VXB can be used for the following five basic roles: armoured personnel carrier, load carrier, light combat vehicle, light reconnaissance vehicle and an anti-riot vehicle. Many types and combinations of armament can be fitted including the following: 90mm gun, 2 × 20mm cannon, 1 × 20mm cannon, 1 × 12.7mm machine gun, 2 × 7.62mm machine guns, 2 single 7.62mm machine guns, 81mm mortar, various anti-tank missile systems and anti-aircraft missile systems. The vehicle can also be used as a command vehicle or ambulance.

Employment

Used by the French Gendarmerie, Gabon, Senegal, Tunisia. Production of the VXB is now complete.

Saviem Creusot-Loire VAB France
Armoured Personnel Carrier

	4 × 4	6 × 6
Crew:	2 + 10	2 + 10
Length:	5.98m	5.98m
Width:	2.49m	2.49m
Height (w/o Armament):	2.06m	2.06m
Ground Clearance:	.4m	.4m
Weight Loaded:	13,000kg	14,000kg
Weight Empty:	11,000kg	12,000kg
Speed (road):	100km/hr	100km/hr
Speed (water):	7km/hr	7km/hr
Range:	1300km	1100km
Fuel:	300 litres	300 litres
Fording:	Amphibious	Amphibious
Vertical Obstacle:	.6m	.6m
Gradient:	60%	60%
Engine:	Saviem HM-71 2356 six cylinder diesel developing 230hp at 2200rpm	

Development

The VAB was developed to meet a requirement issued by the French Army in 1969. Both Panhard and Saviem built prototypes of both 4 × 4 and 6 × 6 vehicles and in 1974 it was announced that Saviem had won the competition. The first production vehicles will be completed in 1977, these will be 4 × 4 models, 6 × 6 models will be placed in production later. Both of these share the same basic hull and automotive components. The VAB is fully amphibious and is propelled in the water by two waterjets at the rear of the hull, a NBC system is fitted as are infra-red driving lights.

Variants

The basic version has been designed for use as an armoured personnel carrier or cargo carrier. Prototypes were armed with a 12.7mm machine gun on a ring mount but production vehicles may be armed with a 20mm cannon. A wide range of armament installations are possible including 7.62mm or 12.7mm machine guns, 20mm cannon (as used on the AMX-10P), turrets as fitted to the Panhard AML series of armoured cars, and various ATGW installations. The vehicle can also be used as an ambulance, command vehicle, radio vehicle or internal security vehicle.

Employment

In production for the French Army.

Top right: The 4 × 4 version of the VAB

Hotchkiss Carriers

France

Data similar to all vehicles: **Fording:** 1m, **V/Obstacle:** .60m, **Trench:** 1.50m, **Gradient:** 60%, **Armour:** 8mm—15mm. All are powered by a Hotchkiss 6 cylinder, OHV, water-cooled petrol engine developing 164hp at 3900rpm. In the above table:

A Reconnaissance Vehicle SP.1A
B Observation & Command Veh. SP.111
C Mortar Carrier SP.1B
D Armoured Ambulance SP.1V

Development
These vehicles were developed from the earlier Hotchkiss TT6 series of carriers. They were built in France for the German Army, although some were also assembled in Germany. All of the above vehicles share the same engine, transmission, track and so on.

Variants
Reconnaissance Vehicle SP.1A: This is armed with a turret-mounted 20m Hispano-Suiza cannon with a 360° traverse, elevation is +75°, depression −10°. Five hundred rounds of 20mm ammunition are carried. This vehicle is designated SPZ 11-2 in the German Army, a similar vehicle is the SPZ 31-2 radio vehicle.

Observation and Command Vehicle SP.111: This is similar to the above vehicle but without the turret. It is armed with a 7.62mm machine gun and carries three radios. The vehicle is designated SPZ 22-2 in the German Army.

Mortar Carrier SP.1B: This has an 81mm mortar firing through the roof, this has an elevation of +45° to +90°, and a traverse of 30° left and 30° right, 50 rounds of mortar ammunition are carried. The vehicle also has a 7.62mm machine gun and 500 rounds of ammunition. It is designated SPZ 51-2 by the German Army. Some have had their mortars removed and an AN/TPS-33 tractical radar system fitted. This model is often called the SPZ 2.

Ambulance SP.1V: This has a crew of three and can carry two stretchers and one sitting patient inside and a further two stretcher patients can be carried on the roof. No armament is fitted. It is designated SPZ 2-2 in the German Army.

Open Cargo Version: This is used by the German Army. It is powered by a 4 cylinder petrol engine and has only four road wheels each side instead of the five per side on the other models. Only the

	A	**B**	**C**	**D**
Crew:	5	5	4/5	3/5
Length:	4.51m	4.51m	4.66m	4.66m
Width:	2.28m	2.28m	2.28m	2.28m
Height:	1.97m	1.69m	1.84m	1.84m
G/Clearance:	.35m	.35m	.35m	.35m
Weight Loaded:	8200kg	7500kg	8200kg	8000kg
G/Pressure:	.58kg.cm²	.55kg.cm²	.58kg.cm²	.57kg.cm²
Speed Road:	58km/ph	58km/ph	58km/ph	58km/ph
Range:	390km	400km	320km	350km
Fuel:	330 litres	345 litres	375 litres	295 litres
Armament:	20mm	7.62mm	7.62mm	7.62mm

front of the vehicle is armoured (engine and driver's compartment).

Experimental Models: Many experimental models were developed to the prototype stage including: 120mm mortar carrier, 90mm tank destroyer, enclosed cargo carrier, armoured personnel carrier and various rocket models.

Employment
These are used only by the German Army. The SPZ 11-2 is being replaced by the new 8 x 8 Spähpanzer 2.

AMX-30 155mm GCT   France

Armament: 1 x 155mm gun, elevation + 66°, depression − 5°, traverse 360°
1 x 7.62mm (or 12.7mm) anti-aircraft machine gun, elevation + 50°, depression − 20°, traverse 360°
2 smoke dischargers mounted either side of turret
42 rounds of 155mm ammunition
2000 rounds of machine gun ammunition
Crew: 4
Length: 10.40m (gun forward)
9.50m (gun rear)
6.485m (hull only)
Width: 3.150m (turret)
3.115m (over hull)
Height: 3.30m (including machine gun)
2.295m (turret top)
G/Clearance: .42m
Engine: Hispano-Suiza HS-110, 12 cylinder multi-fuel water-cooled engine developing 700hp at 2400rpm. This is built in France by Saviem.
Speed: 60km/ph (road)
Range: 450km (road)
Fuel: 970 litres
Fording: 2.20m
V/Obstacle: .93m
Trench: 2.90m
Gradient: 60%
Weight: 41,000kg (loaded)
37,000kg (empty)

Development
The 155mm GCT was shown for the first time at Satory in June 1973. The chassis is a standard AMX-30 with the following modifications; Installation of a cool air ventilation system, artillery communications equipment has been installed and the whole chassis is 2000kg lighter than the standard AMX-30 chassis.

The AMX 30 155mm GCT

The 155mm gun has an automatic loading mechanism which allows the gun to fire a maximum of 8 rounds a minute. It takes three men about half an hour to reload the magazine with a further 42 complete rounds (ie 42 projectiles and 42 cartridges). Its maximum range with TA68 rounds is 23,500m (m/v 810 m/s), or 30,000m using rocket-assisted projectiles currently under development.

The elevation and traverse of the turret is hydraulic, the breach block is of the vertical wedge type and is also hydraulically operated. The vehicle is equipped with an NBC system.

Variants

A German Leopard chassis has also been fitted with the same turret and, according to the GIAT, other MBTs could be fitted with this turret.

Employment

By the end of 1973 two prototypes had been built using an AMX-30 chassis, one prototype with the Leopard chassis and a further ten pre-production 155mm GCTs on AMX-30 chassis were being built. The first trials battery of six guns was formed early in 1974 with production vehicles entering service in 1977/1978.

155mm Self-Propelled Gun MK F3   France
Self-Propelled Howitzer

Armament: 1 x 155mm howitzer, 33 calibre barrel
Crew: 2 (on weapon)
Length: 6.22m (gun forward)
4.88m (chassis only)
Width: 2.72m
Height: 2.10m
G/Clearance: .47m
Weight: 17,400kg (loaded)
G/Pressure: .80kg.cm²
Engine: SOFAM 8GXb 8 cylinder water-cooled petrol engine developing 250hp at 3200rpm
Speed: 65km/pm (road)
Range: 300km (road)
Fuel: 450 litres
Fording: .65m
V/Obstacle: .60m
Trench: 1.50m
Gradient: 50%
Armour: 10mm–40mm

Development/Variants

This weapon consists of a modified AMX chassis on which has been mounted an OB 155-50-BF weapon. The chassis has five road wheels, three return rollers and the driving sprocket at the front; there is no idler at the rear. There are two spades at the rear of the chassis, which are lowered for firing and anchored in the ground by reversing the vehicle.

The gun can have either a 23 calibre or 30 calibre barrel, the latter being the model most found in service. The weapon has a range of 18,500m–21,500m depending on the type of ammunition used. Under development is a round with additional propulsion; this has a range of 25,300m. Types of ammunition available include HE, smoke, illuminating and hollow base. It has a maximum rate of fire of 4 rounds a minute.

Elevation limits are 0° to +67°, traverse being 20° left and 30° right (elevation 0°

to +50°) and 16° left and 30° right (elevation 50° to 67°). When travelling the gun is located 8° to the right.

Trails commenced in 1966 and the vehicle is built by Creusot-Loire. It is fitted with infra-red driving lights.

The weapon is supported in action by an AMX-13 VCI. This carries the rest of the crew of eight men and also carries 25 shells, 25 cartridges and 39 fuzes. In addition this vehicle can tow the ARE 2T F2 ammunition trailer with a further 30 shells and 30 cartridge bags. Another AMX VCI acts as a battery command post and controls four guns.

Employment

Used by Argentina, France, Venezuela, Abu Dhabi, Chile, Ecuador, and Kuwait.

155mm Self-Propelled Gun MK F3 is based on the AMX 13 chassis

105mm Self-Propelled Howitzers France

	Model A (fixed)	Model B (turret)
Crew:	5	5
Length:	6.40m	5.90m
Width:	2.65m	2.50m
Height:	2.70m	2.70m
G/Clearance:	.275–.32m	.34–.45m
Weight Loaded:	16,500kg	17,000kg
G/Pressure:	.80kg/cm²	.82kg.cm²
Speed Road:	60km/ph	60km/ph
Range Road:	350km	300km
Fuel:	415 litres	450 litres
Fording:	.80m	.60m
V/Obstacle:	.66m	.66m
Trench:	1.90m	1.90m
Gradient:	60%	60%
Main Armament Calibre:	105mm	105mm
Anti-Aircraft Calibre:	7.5mm or 7.62mm (2)	7.5mm or 7.62mm (2)
Ammunition 105mm:	56	80
Engine:	Both are powered by a SOFAM 8GXb 8 cylinder water-cooled petrol engine developing 250hp at 3200rpm	
Armour:	10mm–20mm	10mm–20mm

Development/Variants
Self-Propelled Howitzer Mk 61: This was the first model built and is also known as the Model 'A' or Obusier de 105 Model 1950 sur Affût Automoteur by the French. It entered service with the French Army in 1952. It consists of an OB-105-61-AU weapon on a modified AMX chassis. The 105mm howitzer has an elevation of +70° and a depression of −4½°, traverse being 20° left and 20° right. It has a maximum range of 15,000m using the Mk 63 French ammunition, projectile weight being 16kg and m/v 220/670 m/s. Of the 56 rounds carried 6 are anti-tank rounds. Two machine guns are carried, one inside the vehicle and another on top of the vehicle. The latter machine gun can be either on a pintle mount or in a cupola. A total of 2000 rounds of machine gun ammunition are carried. There are both 23 and 30 calibre barrels available.

Self-Propelled Howitzer (turret): This is known as the Model 'B'. The prototype was built in 1961 and so far it has not entered production, although Switzerland has purchased some for trials. It is armed with a 105mm howitzer with a traverse of 360°, the gun can be elevated from −7° to +70°. Of the 80 rounds of ammunition carried 6 are anti-tank rounds. It has a range of 15,000m. Also mounted is an anti-aircraft machine gun, this can be on a pintle mounting or in a cupola. If in a cupola it has a traverse of 360°, elevation being +45° and depression −15°.

Employment
France (23 calibre barrels), Israel, Morocco, Netherlands (30 calibre barrels).

105mm Self-Propelled Howitzer of the French Army (Model A)

AMX-13 DCA
Self-Propelled Anti-Aircraft Gun System

France

Armament: 2 x 30mm Hispano-Suiza HSS 831A guns, elevation + 85°, depression − 8°, traverse 360°
2 x 2 smoke dischargers either side of turret
600 rounds of 30mm ammunition, 300 rounds per barrel
Crew: 3
Length: 5.373m
Width: 2.50m
Height: 3.794m (radar up)
2.716m (radar down)
G /Clearance: .37m
Weight: 17,200kg (loaded)
G /Pressure: .84kg.cm²
Engine: SOFAM 8GXb 8 cylinder water-cooled petrol engine developing 250hp at 3200rpm
Speed: 60km /ph (road)
Range: 300km (road)
Fuel: 450 litres
Fording: .60m
V /Obstacle: .65m
Trench: 1.90m
Gradient: 50%
Armour: 10mm−40mm

Development
Development of the AMX-13 DCA (Défence Centre Avions) started in 1960, the first prototype being completed in 1962. The system entered production in 1964 and went into service with the French Army in 1965.
The system consists of an AMX chassis on which has been mounted a turret with 2 x 30mm cannon. These cannon have a rate of fire of 600 rounds per minute per barrel and an effective range of 3000m. The guns can fire either single, 5, or 15 round bursts, or continuous fire. The guns have a maximum traverse speed of 80° a second and 45° a second in elevation.
Mounted on the rear of the turret is RD 515 Oeil Noir 1 (Black Eye) radar system. This scans through 360° and can pick up targets at a range of 12km and an altitude of 3000m. Sight corrections are controlled by an electric servo-motor and determined by an analogue computer. In addition two periscope sights are provided for use against ground targets.
The system was developed by DTAT, SAMM (turret), Hispano-Suiza (guns) and Thomson-CSF (radar).

Variants
Other anti-aircraft systems on an AMX chassis include:
1. A single 40mm anti-aircraft gun in an armoured turret.
2. 4 x 20mm cannon in an armoured turret with a radar ranging system developed in 1956 /1958 by Oerlikon. Only one was built for trials purposes.
3. AMX-13 DCA but without the radar system.
Employment
In service with the French Army.

Above: *AMX-13 DCA with its radar retracted*

41

Crotale   France

Self-Propelled Anti-Aircraft System (Missile)

Armament: 4 × Crotale surface to air missiles
Crew: 3
Length: 6.22m
Width: 2.65m
Height: 2.04m
G /Clearance: .45m (road)
Weight: 14,800kg (launcher) 12,500kg (acquisition)
Wheelbase: 3.60m
Engine: Each of the four wheels has its own electric motor
Speed: 70km /ph (road)
Range: 500km
Fuel: not applicable
Fording: .68m
V /Obstacle: .30m
Trench: not applicable
Gradient: 40%
Armour: 3mm–5mm

Development/Variants

The Crotale anti-aircraft missile system has been developed by Thomson-CSF, Engins Matra (missiles) and Hotchkiss-Brandt (vehicle). The system was developed from 1964 at the request of the South African Government, who paid a large part of the initial development costs. By 1970 the system was in limited production.

The system comprises two basic vehicles. First the acquisition vehicle with its surveillance radar (range 18km), it also identifies the target and second the firing vehicle. This has four missiles in the ready to fire position, and also tracks the target, launches the missile and guides the missile to its target. Additional launcher vehicles can be added (to a maximum total of three) without needing additional acquisition vehicles. The missile itself has an effective range of over 8.5km and is designed to combat aircraft flying below 3000m. A normal Crotale battery would consist of one acquisition vehicle and two launcher vehicles.

Employment

Crotale is in service with the French Air Force and the South African armed forces where it is known as Cactus, also with Libya, Spain, and Pakistan. A further development of the Crotale is the Shahine, for details of this version refer to entry on AMX-30 MBT.

The Crotale firing and acquisition units in position

Leopard 2 Main Battle Tank   Germany

	Leopard 2	Leopard 2 AV
Crew:	4	4
Length Gun Forward:	9.641m	9.641m
Length of Hull:	7.73m	7.403m
Width:	3.716m	3.54m
Height (turret roof):	2.49m	2.454m
G /Clearance (front):	.54m	.55m
G /Clearance (rear):	.49m	.505m
Weight Loaded:	51,500kg	54,500kg
G /Pressure:	.83kg /cm^2	.91kg /cm^2
Speed Road:	68km /hr	68km /hr
Fording:	1m	1m
Fording with Schnorkel:	4m	4m
V /Obstacle:	1.15m	1.15m
Trench:	3m	3m
Gradient:	60%	60%
Main Armament:	120mm	105mm
Co-axial Armament:	7.62mm	7.62mm
Commander's Armament:	7.62mm	7.62mm
Loader's Armament:	40mm grenade launcher	7.62mm
Engine:	MTU MB 873 Ka-500, 4 stroke multi-fuel engine developing 1500hp at 2600rpm	

Development
The development of the Leopard 2 can be traced back to before the cancellation of the MBT-70 in 1970. Once the MBT-70 was cancelled, development of the Leopard 2 was pushed forward. So far a total of 17 prototypes have been built for the German Army, of these nine had 105mm smooth bore guns whilst the others had 120mm smooth bore guns. In addition, one Leopard 2 AV has been built for the United States Army.

The turret and hull of the Leopard 2 is of the spaced armour type and this gives much improved protection against anti-tank weapons, especially anti-tank guided missiles. The engine used in the Leopard 2 is a further development of the engine used in the German models of the MBT-70, this gives the tank a power-to-weight ratio of 30bhp /t and an outstanding cross country capability. Equipment fitted to the Leopard 2 includes a stabilised commander's periscope, combined laser and stereoscopic rangefinder for the gunner, heater, infra-red searchlight which is stowed under armour in the turret bustle when not required, passive night vision equipment (this is also stowed under armour when not required), stabilised main armament, NBC system and night driving equipment.

Two types of ammunition have been developed for the 120mm smooth bore gun. One is of the APFSDS type for use against armour targets and the other is a multi-purpose round for use against other battlefield targets. Loading is hydraulically assisted. The 120mm gun has an elevation of + 20° and a depression of − 9°. A total of 40 rounds of 120mm and 3000 rounds of 7.62mm ammunition are carried. The commander's 7.62mm machine gun can be aimed and fired from within the turret, this has a maximum elevation of + 65° and a depression of − 15°. The 40mm grenade launcher in the loader's hatch will probably be replaced by a 7.62mm machine gun on a pintle mount, this will have an elevation of + 65° and a depression of − 10°, total traverse being 360°.

The power pack contains the engine, transmission and cooling system and can be removed from the vehicle as a complete unit in about 15 minutes.

Variants
The basic chassis could be adapted to accept the turret mounted on the Gepard anti-aircraft tank.

The Leopard 2 delivered to the United States is designated the Leopard 2 AV, the latter standing for 'Austere Version'. This has been designed to meet the requirements of the United States Army. It differs from the German Leopard 2 in a number of significant areas. First it is armed with a standard 105mm rifled tank gun in a new turret, it has a much simpler fire control system than the Leopard 2 and various other detailed modifications have been carried out.

Employment
Trials. Not yet in production.

Top: *Leopard 2 MBT with 105mm smooth bore gun*

Above: *Leopard 2 MBT with 120mm smooth bore gun*

Below: *Leopard 2 AV with 105mm rifled tank gun*

Leopard A2 and A3 Main Battle Tank   Germany

Armament: 1 × 105mm L-7A3 gun, elevation +20°, depression −9° (stabilised)
1 × 7.62mm co-axial machine gun
1 × 7.62mm anti-aircraft machine gun
4 smoke dischargers mounted either side of turret
60 rounds of 105mm ammunition
5500 rounds of 7.62mm machine gun ammunition
Crew: 4
Length: 9.54m (gun forward)
6.94m (hull only)
Width: 3.25m (3.40m with skirts)
Height: 2.64m (top of cupola)
2.40m (turret roof)
G/Clearance: .44m
Weight: 42,400kg (loaded)
40,400kg (empty)
G/Pressure: .90kg.cm²
Engine: MTU MB 838 Ca.M500, 10 cylinder, multi-fuel engine developing 830hp at 2200rpm
Speed: 65km/ph (road)
Range: 600km (road)
450km (cross country)
Fuel: 985 litres
Fording: 2.25m
4.00m (with schnorkel)
V/Obstacle: 1.15m
Trench: 3.00m
Gradient: 60%
Armour: 10mm−60mm (estimate)

Development
The development of the Leopard can be traced back as far as 1956 when France, Germany and Italy formulated requirements for a standard tank. In the end France built the AMX-30, Germany the Leopard and Italy the M-60A1 (only to purchase the Leopard in 1970). Prototypes were completed by two groups in Germany, Group 'A' in June 1960 and Group 'B' in August 1960. After extensive evaluation the contract was awarded to Group 'B' and the prime contractor was Krauss-Maffei AG. The first production Leopard was completed on 9th September 1965. There are the following models of the basic gun tank: Leopard A1 (series 1 through 4), Leopard A2, Leopard A3 with a new turret of welded construction and numerous other modifications (5th production batch, 110 built) and the Leopard A4 (6th production batch, 250 built), the Leopard A4 is similar to the A3 but has an integrated fire control system and a fully automatic gearbox. The Leopard has a NBC system and a full range of night fighting and night driving aids, in addition it can be fitted with a schnorkel for deep wading.

Variants
Armoured Recovery Vehicle: This is basically a Leopard chassis fitted with a superstructure, dozer blade, winch with 90m of cable and a maximum capacity of 35,000kg, and a crane with a traverse of 270° and a maximum lifting capacity of 20,000kg. Armament consists of a 7.62mm A/A machine gun and a 7.62mm bow machine gun, and smoke dischargers. Data is similar to the Leopard MBT except:
Length: 7.57m (travelling)
Width: 3.25m
Height: 2.69m (inc. A/A mg)
G/Clearance: .44m
G/Pressure: .815kg.cm²
Weight: 39,800kg (loaded)
37,800kg (empty)
Range: 800km (road)
Fuel: 1570 litres
Fording: 2.10m

Armoured Pioneer Vehicle: This is very similar to the armoured recovery vehicle but it has an earth boring tool and the dozer blade can be fitted with excavating teeth. Data is similar to the ARV except that it has a loaded weight of 40,800kg and an empty weight of 38,800kg.
New Engineer Vehicle: Undergoing trials late in 1976 were 2 new engineer vehicles designed specifically for operations on river banks.
Rocket Launcher: A Leopard chassis is being used as a test rig for a 6 barrelled rocket launcher.
Anti-Aircraft Vehicle: See separate entry.
Bridgelayer: Two models of this were built in 1969. These were known as the Model 'A' and Model 'B'. The production version is the Model 'B' and this entered service in 1973 with the German Army. It has a loaded weight of 45,300kg and its bridge is 22m long when in position. Other data is similar to the MBT except:
Crew: 2
Length: 11.40m (with bridge)
10.30m (w/o bridge)
Width: 4.00m (with bridge)
Height: 3.50m (with bridge)
2.56m (w/o bridge)
G/Pressure: .96kg.cm²
Bridge Capacity: 50,000kg
Training Tank: This is simply a Leopard MBT with its turret removed and a cab fitted. It is used for training drivers. Loaded weight is about 40,000kg.
Self-Propelled Gun: Under test in 1973 was a Leopard Chassis fitted with the turret mounting a 155mm gun as fitted to the AMX-30 155mm GCT self-propelled gun.

Employment

Used by Germany (and ARV, Pioneer, Bridgelayer), Belgium (and ARV, Pioneer, Training), Norway (and ARV), Netherlands (ARV and Training), Italy (ARV and Pioneer —600 Leopards are being built in Italy and 200 have been purchased from Germany).

By 1975 3637 Leopard MBTs and 682 ARV and Pioneer Leopards had been built, production is continuing for Canada, Australia and Denmark. Both Greece and Turkey will probably place orders for the Leopard and it may be built under licence in these countries.

Left: *Leopard MBTs of the German Army*

Below: *Leopard A2*

Top right: *Leopard A4 has a chassis similar to that of the Leopard A2 but has a new turret with spaced armour*

Centre right: *Leopard Armoured Recovery Vehicle recovering another Leopard*

Bottom right: *Leopard Engineer Tank, the auger on the rear deck is for making holes in the ground*

TAM Medium Battle Tank   Germany

Armament: 1 × 105mm gun
1 × 7.62mm machine gun co-axial with main armament
1 × 7.62mm anti-aircraft machine gun
2 × 4 smoke dischargers
Crew: 4
Length: 8.12m (gun forward)
6.57m (hull)
Width: 3.12m
Height: 2.4m (turret top)
G/Clearance: .44m
Weight: 29,500kg (loaded)
G/Pressure: .79kg/cm²
Engine: MTU MB 833 Ea-500 6 cylinder diesel developing 600hp at 2200rpm
Speed: 75km/hr
Range: 600km
1000km (long range fuel tanks)
Fording: 1.5m
4m (with kit)
V/Obstacle: 1m
Trench: 2.5m
Gradient: 60%

Development

The first prototype of the TAM Medium Battle Tank was completed at the Kassel Works of Thyssen Henschel (previously known as Rheinstahl AG) in September, 1976. The TAM is essentially a modified Marder chassis with a new turret mounting a standard 105mm rifled tank gun. The main armament is fully stabilised and both the commander and gunner are provided with equipment for aiming and firing the gun. A total of 50 rounds of 105mm ammunition are carried, 20 in the turret and a further 30 in the hull. The range of the TAM can be extended by the fitting of long range fuel tanks at the rear of the hull.

The TAM Medium Battle Tank is aimed primarily at the export market as the manufacturers feel that many countries cannot afford the current range of MBT's, and in any case many countries, especially in South America and the Far East, have roads and bridges that cannot take the 40–50 ton weight of current main battle tanks.

Employment

Trials.

Below: *The first prototype of the TAM Medium Battle Tank*

Spähpanzer Luchs
Reconnaissance Vehicle

Germany

Armament: 1 × 20mm Rh.202 cannon with an elevation of +80° and a depression of −15°, traverse 360°.
1 × 7.62mm MG3 anti-aircraft machine gun
2 × 4 smoke dischargers each side of turret
Crew: 4
Length: 7.743m
Width: 2.98m
Height: 2.905m (cupola top)
2.125m (hull top)
G/Clearance: .556m (hull)
Weight: 19,500kg (loaded)
Track: 2.54m
Engine: Daimler Benz Model OM 403 VA 10 cylinder multi-fuel engine developing 390hp at 2500rpm
Speed: 90km/hr
9km/hr (water)
Range: 800km
Fuel: 500 litres
Fording: Amphibious
V/Obstacle: .6m
Trench: 1.9m
Gradient: 60%

Development
In 1964 the German Army laid the foundations for a new range of vehicles which were to have included an 8 × 8 reconnaissance vehicle, 4 × 4 and 6 × 6 armoured load carriers and a whole range of 4 × 4, 6 × 6 and 8 × 8 trucks, all of these would share many common components. Prototypes of the 8 × 8 reconnaissance vehicle (Spähpanzer 2) were built by Daimler Benz and a consortium of companies known as the Joint Project Office. The production contract was awarded to Rheinstahl (now Thyssen-Henschel) in December, 1973, and the first production vehicle was completed in May 1975, and the last of 408 vehicles should be completed late in 1977. It has now started to replace the Hotchkiss Spz 11-2 reconnaissance vehicle in the German Army.

The vehicle is fully amphibious being propelled in the water by two propellers at the rear of the hull. An NBC system is fitted as is a full range of night vision equipment. The vehicle has full 8 × 8 drive and can also be driven backwards at maximum speed. The crew of four consists of front driver, commander and gunner in the turret, and rear driver/radio operator.

Variants
There are no variants of the Luchs. There was to have been a 4 × 4 Spähpanzer 3 but this has not yet been built. This would have the same turret as the Spähpanzer 2 and would weigh 10,600kg. Other data: Crew 4, length 5.95m, width 2.5m, height 2.5m, maximum road speed 90km/hr, water speed 10 km/hr, range 800km and gradient 60%.

Employment
In service with the German Army.

Above: *The Spähpanzer Luchs 8 × 8 reconnaissance vehicle*

HWK 10 Series   Germany

Armament: 1 × 7.62mm or 1 × 12.7mm machine gun
Crew: 2 + 10
Length: 5.05m
Width: 2.58m
Height: 1.585m (w/o machine gun)
G/Clearance: .435m
Weight: 11,000kg (loaded)
9,000kg (empty)
G/Pressure: .55kg.cm^2
Engine: Chrysler 361B, 8 cylinder petrol engine developing 211hp at 4000rpm
Speed: 65km/ph (road)
Range: 320km (road)
Fuel: 300 litres
Fording: 1.20m
V/Obstacle: .68m
Trench: 2.00m
Gradient: 60%
Armour: 8mm–14.5mm
Note. *The data relates to the HWK 11 APC.*

Development
The HWK 10 series of light tracked vehicles were designed in the early 1960s as a private venture by Henschel-Werke (now Thyssen-Henschel). The first proto-types of the HWK 11 were built in 1963 and these were followed by 40 production vehicles for export, in 1964. Only two HWK 13s were built. The hull of the HWK 11 is of all-welded construction and is proof against 7.62mm ammunition. The driver and commander have individual hatches, the crew have overhead hatches enabling them to fire their weapons from within the vehicle and there are two large doors at the rear of the vehicle. The vehicle is not fitted with an NBC system and it can be fitted with infra-red driving lights. It is not amphibious, capable only of fording.

Variants
HWK 10   Armed with 10 anti-tank guided missiles.
HWK 11   Armoured personnel carrier.
HWK 12   Anti-tank vehicle armed with a turret-mounted 90mm gun.
HWK 13   Reconnaissance vehicle armed with a turret-mounted 20mm cannon.
HWK 14   Mortar carrier with an 81mm or 105mm mortar.
HWK 15   Wireless, command or artillery fire control vehicle.
HWK 16   Ambulance, no armament fitted.

Employment
Used only by Mexico.

The HWK 11 Armoured Personnel Carrier

Schützenpanzer, Neu Marder

Germany

Mechanised Infantry Combat Vehicle

Armament: 1 × 20mm Rh 202 cannon, elevation + 65°, depression − 17°
1 × 7.62mm MG 3 co-axial machine gun
1 × 7.62mm MG 3 machine gun at rear of vehicle
6 smoke dischargers on the turret
1250 rounds of 20mm ammunition
5000 rounds of 7.62mm ammunition
Crew: 10
Length: 6.79m
Width: 3.24m
Height: 2.95m (inc. searchlight)
2.86m (turret top)
G/Clearance: .45m
Weight: 28,200kg (loaded)
G/Pressure: .80kg.cm^2
Engine: MTU MB 833 Ea-500, 6 cylinder diesel developing 600hp at 2200rpm
Speed: 75 + km/ph (road)
Range: 520km (road)
Fuel: 652 litres
Fording: 1.50m
2.50m (with kit)
V/Obstacle: 1.00m
Trench: 2.50m
Gradient: 60%

Development

The requirements for a new infantry combat vehicle for the German Army were drawn up in 1959. The first contracts for the construction of prototype vehicles were awarded in 1960 to Rheinstahl, Henschel and Mowag (Switzerland). These were the first prototype series. They were followed by the second prototype series in 1961/1963. In 1967 a further 10 prototypes were built, these being known as the third series. In October 1969 a contract was awarded to Rheinstahl (now Thyssen-Henschel) for the production of 1926 vehicles, of which Atlas MaK of Kiel would build 875 vehicles. The first vehicle was handed over on 7th May 1971. The Marder can also be used as a load carrier or ambulance.

The Marder, is without doubt, the most advanced Infantry Combat Vehicle in the West. It is fitted with an NBC system and a full range of night driving and night fighting equipment. Under development is an amphibious kit enabling the vehicle to cross rivers that are too deep to ford.

The crew are provided with roof hatches and there is a single ramp at the rear of the vehicle. Either side of the hull are two ball type mountings that allow the crew to fire their weapons from inside the vehicle. The two turrets can be used against both ground and air targets. A Milan ATGW can be mounted on the turret.

The Marder mechanised infantry combat vehicle

Variants

Schützenpanzer, Neu, Mörserträger:
This has a crew of 4/5 men and is armed
with a 120mm Tampella mortar and 2 ×
7.62mm machine guns. One hundred
rounds of mortar ammunition and 6000
rounds of machine gun ammunition are
carried. Performance figures are similar to
those of the Marder. It has a loaded weight
of 25,500kg. This vehicle completed its
trials in 1970 but no production order has
been given. Rheinstahl have, however,
converted over 500 M-113 APCs to carry
the 120mm mortar.

**Schützenpanzer, Neu, Waffenträger
ROLAND:** It consists of a Marder
chassis on which has been mounted the
Roland anti-aircraft missile system developed by Germany and France. Roland 1
is a clear-weather system and Roland 2
an all weather system. Two missiles are
carried in the ready to fire position with
a further eight missiles in the hull. Roland
has also been tested in the United States.
So far four prototypes have been built and
another eight prototypes are being built.
In 1975 the German Army placed an order
for 143 Roland SAM systems on the
Marder chassis. These should enter service
in 1979.

Marder with Rapier: Shown at Farnborough air display in 1970 was a model
of the Marder fitted with the British Aircraft Corporation Rapier anti-aircraft
missile system. It is a project only.

Radarpanzer: Development stopped.

Marder with new turret: Undergoing
trials is a Marder with a three axis stabilised turret. This is hydraulically operated
and electronically controlled.

TAM: There is a separate entry for the
TAM tank which uses the Marder chassis.

Employment
Used only by the German Army.

Schützenpanzer, SPZ 12-3
Armoured Personnel Carrier

Germany

Armament: 1 × 20mm Hispano-Suiza
820 gun, elevation +75°, depression
−10°
1 × 7.62mm machine gun (optional)
2 × 4 smoke grenade launchers
2000 rounds of 20mm ammunition
Crew: 2 + 6
Length: 6.31mm (including gun)
5.56m (hull only)
Width: 2.54m
Height: 1.85m (including turret)
1.63m (without turret)
G/Clearance: .40m
Weight: 14,600kg (loaded)
G/Pressure: .75kg.cm^2
Engine: Rolls-Royce B 81 Mk 80F, 8

cylinder petrol engine developing 235hp
at 3800rpm
Speed: 58km/ph (road)
Range: 270km
Fuel: 340 litres
Fording: .70m
V/Obstacle: .60m
Trench: 1.60m
Gradient: 58%
Armour: 8mm−30mm

Development
The SPZ 12-3 (or Hispano-Suiza 30) was
originally developed as a private venture
by Hispano-Suiza of Switzerland. The
chassis started off as an anti-aircraft

vehicle. For a number of reasons production of the vehicle was undertaken in England (by Leyland Motors) and Germany (Henschel and Hanomag). It was in production from 1958 to 1962. All models have a British built engine, the 20mm cannon was made in Germany by Rheinmetall. The SPZ 12-3 does not have an NBC system, the vehicle is however fitted with infra-red driving lights. In 1971 there were still over 1800 of these vehicles in service. Hispano-Suiza projects included a 90mm tank destroyer, light tank with a 90mm gun, various anti-aircraft vehicles and a rocket launcher vehicle. Variants used by the German Army are listed below.

Variants

SPZ 12-3 with 106mm Recoilless Rifle: This is a standard SPZ 12-3 fitted with the American M-40A1 106mm recoilless rifle over the rear of the vehicle. It retains its 20mm gun turret. Weight is 14,300kg.

Jagdpanzer Rakete (JPZ 3-3): This has similar data to the basic APC and has a crew of three, loaded weight is 13,100kg. No turret is fitted on this model. Armament consists of two launching rails for SS 11 ATGW.

SPZ 52-3 Panzermörser: This vehicle is armed with a French 120mm mortar firing through the roof of the vehicle. The turret has been removed and the only armament fitted is a 7.62mm machine gun which is provided with a shield. It has a crew of four, height is 2.13m including the mortar.

SPZ 51-3 Morserträger: Armed with an 81mm mortar firing through the roof of the vehicle. It was not placed in production.

SPZ 21-3 Funkpanzer: This is a command and radio vehicle.

SPZ 81-3 Feuerleitpanzer: This is an artillery fire control vehicle and can also be used as a command post.

SPZ 12-3 with TOW system: In 1971 tests were started of an SPZ 12-3 with its turret removed and a TOW ATGW system installed. The installation being called PARS-3. Some have been fitted with the Milan ATGW for trials.

Employment

Used only by the German Army.

HS-30 APC with 20mm gun at maximum elevation

UR-416 Armoured Personnel Carrier　　　Germany

Armament: 1 × 7.62mm machine gun, elevation + 75°, depression − 10°
Crew: 2 + 8
Length: 4.99m
Width: 2.26m
Height: 2.24m (w/o machine gun) 2.18m (hull top)
G/Clearance: .44m (differential)
Weight: 6300kg (loaded) 4800kg (empty)
Track: 1.616m
Engine: DB OM-352, 6 cylinder, water-cooled, in-line, diesel developing 110hp at 2800rpm
Speed: 80km/ph (road)
Range: 700km (road)
Fuel: 150 litres
Fording: 1.00m
V/Obstacle: .55m
Trench: nil
Gradient: 70%
Armour: 9mm
Wheelbase: 2.90m

Development
The UR-416 has been designed by Rheinstahl (now Thyssen-Henschel) primarily for internal security duties and border patrols. The first prototype was completed in 1965 and series production commenced in 1969. The chassis used is that of the famous Daimler-Benz Unimog; this is a 4 × 4 (cross country) or 4 × 2 (road vehicle. The hull can be easily separated from the chassis for maintenance purposes. The hull is of all welded construction and doors are provided in the sides and rear of the vehicle, in addition there are hatches in the roof and firing ports are provided at the sides and rear of the vehicle. Optional extras include radios, various types of tyres and a winch.

Variants
The following versions of the basic armoured personnel carrier have been developed by Rheinstahl:
Ambulance: Carrying 8 sitting, or 4 stretcher, or 4 sitting and 2 stretcher patients.
Command: Crew of 4 with various radios, mapboards etc.

A UR-416 armed with turret mounted 20mm Rh.202 cannon

Scout Car: Various versions armed with: single turret mounted 7.62mm machine gun
twin turret mounted 7.62mm machine guns
single turret mounted cannon (two versions)
single turret mounted 90mm recoilless rifle
single turret mounted 20mm Rh.202 cannon.
Missile: Two versions: COBRA anti-tank missile vehicle
TOW anti-tank missile vehicle.

Maintenance: Has a jib at the front, welding equipment, benches and tools.
Police: Three types of police vehicle have been designed:
Fitted with obstacle clearing blade at the front
Fitted with observation Cupola Model I
Fitted with observation Cupola Model II.
Employment
Over 400 UR-416s have been built for customers in Europe, South America, Africa and Asia (inc. Netherlands, Peru).

Jagdpanzer Kanone (JPZ 4-5) Germany
Self-Propelled Anti-Tank Gun

Armament: 1 x 90mm gun, elevation + 15°, depression − 8°, traverse 15° left and 15° right
1 x 7.62mm co-axial machine gun
1 x 7.62mm anti-aircraft machine gun
8 smoke dischargers
51 rounds of 90mm ammunition
4000 rounds of 7.62mm ammunition
Crew: 4
Length: 8.75m (including gun)
6.238m (hull only)
Width: 2.98m
Height: 2.085m (w/o A/A machine gun)
G/Clearance: .45m (front)
.44m (rear)
Weight: 25,700kg (loaded)
G/Pressure: .75kg.cm² (loaded)
Engine: Daimler-Benz, MB 837, 8 cylinder diesel developing 500hp at 2000rpm
Speed: 70km/ph (road)
Range: 400km (road)

Fuel: 470 litres
Fording: 1.40m
2.10m (with kit)
V/Obstacle: .75m
Trench: 2.00m
Gradient: 60%
Armour: 50mm (maximum)

Development
This vehicle uses the same chassis as the Jagdpanzer Rakete. Design of the JPZ 4-5 started in the late 1950s and the first prototypes were built by Hanomag (1 RU 3/1, 1 RU 3/2), Henschel (1 HK 3/1, 1 HK 3/2) and Mowag (HM 3), these were known as the first series. They were followed by the second series built by Hanomag and Henschel in 1963/64. Last

The Jagdpanzer Kanone (JPZ 4-5). Note the 7.62mm machine gun on the roof of the vehicle

came the third series from Hanomag (RU 331-333) and Henschel (RU 334-336). The vehicle was then ordered in quantity. A total of 750 vehicles have been built for the German Army by Rheinstahl-Hanomag and Rheinstahl-Henschel, production ran from 1965 to 1967. In 1972 Belgium ordered 80 of these to be assembled in Belgium for the Belgian Army. The Belgian vehicles will have modernised transmission and suspension system (using Marder components) and an improved fire control system which includes laser rangefinder a Lyran launcher for launching flares has also been fitted. The vehicle has a hull of all welded steel. An NBC system is fitted and infra-red driving and fighting lights can be fitted. The 90mm gun has an effective combat range of 2000m and fires HEAT-T and HEP-T rounds, maximum stated rate of fire is 12 rounds a minute. The gun is elevated and traversed by hand, a double baffle muzzle brake is fitted.

Variants
The Jagdpanzer Rakete has the same hull. Other variants that have not reached production include a multiple rocket launcher system, an anti-aircraft vehicle and a reconnaissance tank (Spähpanzer) Thyssen-Henschel have suggested that the JP2 4-5 could be refitted with a 105mm gun.

Employment
Used by the Belgian and German Armies.

Jagdpanzer Rakete (RJPZ-2)   Germany
Missile Armed Anti-Tank Vehicle

Armament: 2 × launchers for SS 11 ATGW
1 × 7.62mm bow machine gun
1 × 7.62mm anti-aircraft machine gun
8 smoke dischargers
14 SS 11 ATGW carried
3200 rounds of 7.62mm ammunition
Crew: 4
Length: 6.43m
Width: 2.98m
Height: 2.60m (with missiles)
1.98m (hull top)
G/Clearance: .43m
Weight: 23,000kg (loaded)
G/Pressure: .63kg.cm^2
Engine: Daimler-Benz, 8 cylinder diesel, Model MB-837 developing 500hp at 2000rpm
Speed: 70km/ph (road)
Range: 400km (road)
Fuel: 470 litres
Fording: 1.40m
2.10m (with kit)
V/Obstacle: .75m
Trench: 2.00m
Gradient: 60%

Development
The hull of the Jagdpanzer Rakete is almost the same as that of the Jagdpanzer Kanone. The hull is of all welded construction and an NBC system is fitted. Infra-red driving lights are fitted. The first prototype was the RU 234 by Hanomag, this was followed by the RU 341, 342 and 343 (all by Hanomag) and the RU 344, 345 and 346 (all by Henschel). Production started in 1967 and 370 have been built for the German Army. The left launcher can be traversed from 270° to 360° and the right launcher from 0° to 90°, thus covering a 180° arc at the front of the vehicle. Elevation is from 0° to +20°. The SS 11 missiles are reloaded from within the vehicle and have an effective range of 3000m. The 7.62mm machine gun mounted in the bow of the vehicle has a traverse of 15° left and 15° right, elevation is +15° and depression −8°.

Variants
All RJPZ-2s of the German army will be refitted with the HOT installation between 1977–1982. The German/French HOT ATGW has a range of 75m–4000m. This has two launcher shoes and a single periscope, the empty tubes are ejected after the missile has been fired.

Employment
In service only with the German Army.

Right: *A Jagdpanzer Rakete with the Hot ATGW*

Below left: *Jagdpanzer Rakete with SS-11 ATGW on one of its launchers*

Flakpanzer 1 (Gepard)

Germany

Armament: 2 × 35mm belt-fed Oerlikon cannon, elevation + 85°, depression − 5°, traverse 360°
4 smoke dischargers mounted each side of the turret
640 rounds of 35mm ammunition for A/A use and 40 rounds of 35mm AP ammunition
Crew: 3
Length: 7.70m (guns forward)
7.27m (gun rearward)
Width: 3.25m
Height: 3.07m (radar retracted)
Weight: 45,000kg (loaded)
43,500kg (empty)
G/Pressure: 0.95kg/cm²
Engine: MTU MB 835 Ca.M500, 10 cylinder multi-fuel engine developing 830hp at 2200rpm. A 95hp auxiliary engine is also fitted
Speed: 65km/hr (road)
Range: 600km (road)
450km (cross country)
Fuel: 985 litres
Fording: 2.25m
V/Obstacle: 1.15m
Trench: 3.00m
Gradient: 60%

Below: *The Gepard all weather anti-aircraft gun system*

Development/Variants

The Gepard is an autonomous all weather anti-aircraft gun system for defence against low flying aircraft, and can be switched within seconds from an anti-aircraft to an anti-tank role.

The first prototype 5PZF-A was delivered in 1968 and tested the following year, the participating companies were: Oerlikon for the turret and armament, Contraves for the computer and integration, Siemens-Albis for the target tracking radar, Hollandse for the search radar and Krauss-Maffei for the chassis and power supply system. In 1969 a further four prototypes were ordered. These were designated 5PZF-B. At about the same time the Netherlands Army became interested in the vehicle and they ordered a model known as the 5PZF-C, these differ only in their make and type of radar system. After some very successful trials 12 pre-production 5PZF-B's were ordered by Germany in 1970 followed by an order from the Netherlands for 5 5PZF-C's. The 5PZF-B has a search radar developed by Siemens and a tracking radar developed by Siemens-Albis whilst the 5PFZ-C has an integrated search and track radar by Hollandse. Both of these systems have radars with a range of 15km approx. If required the search antenna can be folded down behind the turret and the tracking antenna can be turned towards the turret in an armoured position. The guns fire at the rate of 550 rounds per gun and can be fired as single shots, controlled bursts or long bursts. Of the 680 rounds carried, 640 are for anti-aircraft use and 40 are for ground use, the latter being carried in an external armoured magazine. Krauss-Maffei is the prime contractor for series production.

Employment

On order for Belgium, German and the Netherlands. Deliveries to the German Army commenced late in 1976.

Transportpanzer
Armoured Cargo Vehicle/APC

Germany

Armament: 1 x 20mm Rh.202 cannon with a traverse of 360°
Crew: 2 + 10/12
Length: 6.76m
Width: 2.98m
Height: 2.3m (top of hull)
G/Clearance: .46m (axles)
Weight: 16,000kg (loaded)
14,000kg (empty)
Track: 2.54m (front)
2.56m (rear)
Engine: Daimler Benz diesel developing 320hp at 2500rpm

Speed: 87km/hr
8km/hr (water)
Range: 800km
Fording: Amphibious
Gradient: 60%

Development

Prototypes of both a 4 x 4 (Transportpanzer 2) and a 6 x 6 (Transport-

Below: *One of the prototypes of the 6 x 6 Transportpanzer 1 vehicle*

panzer 1) were completed some years ago, these shared many common components with the Spähpanzer 8 × 8 reconnaissance vehicle and a new range of tactical trucks. It is now reported that the 6 × 6 model will soon be placed in production, whilst no decision has been taken on the 4 × 4 model. This vehicle will fulfil a wide variety of roles on the battlefield including carrying men, supplies and ammunition. It will perform a similar role to the French Saviem VAB vehicles which have recently been placed in production for the French Army.

The vehicle is fully amphibious being propelled in the water by two propellors at the rear of the hull. Before entering the water a trim vane is erected at the front of the hull. It has been designed to carry between 2000–3000kg of cargo or a maximum of 12 men. Cargo can be loaded through the twin doors at the rear of the hull (1.34m wide and 1.25m high) or through two smaller hatches in the roof.

The armament installation consists of a 20mm cannon, this being mounted in the centre of the roof, other armament installations are possible, for example a 7.62mm machine gun over one of the forward hatches. Steering is power assisted on the front four wheels. A NBC system is provided as is night vision equipment. The commander and driver are seated at the front of the hull, with the powerpack to their rear, and the cargo/personnel compartment at the rear of the hull.

Variants

No variants have been announced, although some are no doubt under development.

Employment

Not yet in service.

Shir Iran Great Britain

The first Iranian order was for some 800 Chieftain Mk. 3/3/(P), Mk. 5/5(P), armoured recovery vehicles and bridgelayers. In December 1974 Iran placed a further order for up to 1200 tanks of an improved design. In June, 1976, it was announced that this would be called the Shir Iran (or Lion of Iran). This second batch will also be built at the Royal Ordnance Factory at Leeds. The new Shir Iran will be powered by a new Rolls Royce model CV12TCA 12 cylinder diesel which develops 1200hp at 2300rpm, this engine was first shown at Aldershot in June 1976. The engine will be coupled to a new David Brown TN37 automatic transmission which incorporates a torque converter. The cooling group has been designed by Airscrew Holden Limited whilst Dunlop have developed a hydropneumatic suspension system. The first production models are expected to be completed in 1977/78.

The Shir Iran will also incorporate the new Chobham Armour which was revealed in June 1976. This is of the laminate type rather than of the spaced type which has been used in tanks such as the Leopard 2.

The tank will have the same armament as the standard Chieftain but a new barrel made of Electro-Slag Refined (ESR) steel is being developed, this will have an increased barrel life. A new range of ammu-

Below: A Chieftain trials tank fitted with the new Chobham Armour

nition is being developed for the Chieftain, this will be used for both British Army Chieftains and for Iranian Chieftains, the following types are being developed at the Royal Armament Research and Development Establishment at Fort Halstead, Kent:

Canister

Armour Piercing Fin Stabilised Discarding Sabot (APFSDS)

Armour Piercing Discarding Sabot (Product Improved)

High Explosive Anti-Tank

High Explosive Squash Head (Product Improved)

Illuminating

Smoke (Product Improved)

The Shir Iran will also be fitted with the new Marconi Improved Fire Control System (this will also be retrofitted to British Army Chieftains). This system comprises four main components—data handling subsystem, sighting subsystem, sensor subsystem and a new gun control system. A new cupola designed the No. 21 has been developed by the MEL Company. This incorporates a L37 GPMG which has a depression of $-10°$ and an elevation of $+90°$, this can be aimed and fired from within the vehicle. This incorporates a thermal pointer and a light intensifier night sight. It is not known at the present time if this will be incorporated into the Chieftains being built for Iran. From the limited amount of information which has been released on the Shir Iran it is apparent this will in effect be a new tank, although it will retain the powerful 120mm gun as used on the standard Chieftain MBT, this is capable of knocking out any known armoured fighting vehicles out to some 3000m.

Chieftain Mk 3 Main Battle Tank   Great Britain

Armament: 1 × 120mm gun L 11A2, elevation + 20°, depression − 10°
1 × 12.7mm ranging machine gun
1 × 7.62mm L8 A1 co-axial machine gun
1 × 7.62mm L37 A1 machine gun (commander's cupola)
2 × 6 barrelled smoke dischargers
53 rounds of 120mm ammunition
600 rounds of 12.7mm ranging machine gun ammunition
6000 rounds of 7.62mm ammunition
Crew: 4
Length: 10.79m (gun forward)
7.52m (hull only)
Width: 3.66m (inc searchlight)
3.50m (over skirts)
Height: 2.89m (inc commander's mg)
G /Clearance: .51m

Weight: 54,100kg (loaded)
51,460kg (empty)
G /Pressure: .843kg.cm²
Engine: Leyland L60 No. 4 Mk 5A, 6 cylinder, multi-fuel engine developing 730bhp at 2100rpm
Speed: 48km /ph (road)
Range: 500km (road)
300km (cross country)
Fuel: 950 litres
Fording: 1.07m
4.57m (schnorkel)
V /Obstacle: .914m
Trench: 3.15m
Gradient: 60%
Armour: 150mm (estimate)

The Chieftain Armoured Recovery Vehicle

Development

The Chieftain (FV 4201) was developed to replace the Centurion MBT. The first prototype Chieftain was completed in 1959, and was first shown to the public in 1961. In May 1963, the Chieftain was accepted for service and two production lines were set up, one at the Royal Ordnance Factory, Leeds and the other at Vickers Elswick Works. Vickers are the design parents of the Chieftain. The Chieftain is fitted with an NBC system, a full range of night vision devices, a dozer kit is available and a schnorkel can be fitted. A ranging machine gun is fitted, although more recent models have in addition a laser rangefinder. The gun is stabilised and can be fired accurately whilst on the move; types of ammunition carried are APDS and HESH, with bagged charges.

Variants

Mk 1: This was introduced in 1965 for training purposes, 585bhp engine.
Mk 1/2: This is a Mk 1 modified to Mk 2 standards for training purposes.

Mk 1/3: This is a Mk 1 with a new power-pack, for training purposes.
Mk 1/4: This is a Mk 1/2 with a new powerpack, modified ranging mg, used for training.
Mk 2: This was the first model to enter service in 1966, 650bhp engine.
Mk 3: This entered service in 1969 and has an improved auxiliary generator, improved engine and a No. 15 Mk 2 cupola with L37 machine gun.
Mk 3/G: Prototype with turret air breathing.
Mk 3/2: This is a modified Mk 3/G.
Mk 3/S: Modified Mk 3/G (production), turret air breathing.
Mk 3/3: This is a Mk 3 with extended range ranging machine gun (2500m), laser range-finder, improved engine and a new air cleaner system.
Mk 3/3(P): This is a Mk 3/3 with a number of modifications for Iran.
Mk 4: Prototype only, had additional fuel and less ranging mg ammunition.
Mk 5: This is a Mk 3/3 with many

The Chieftain Armoured Vehicle Launched Bridge laying bridge

A Chieftain of the Blues and Royals

improvements including an improved engine and gearbox, increased ammunition stowage (64 rounds carried).

Mk 5/5(P): This is a Mk 5 for Iran with modifications.

Mk 6: This is the Mk 2 with new powerpack and modified ranging machine gun.

Mk 7: This is Mk 3, Mk 3/G, Mk 3/2 and Mk 3/S with modified ranging machine gun and improved powerpack.

Mk 8: This is the Mk 3/3 with above modifications.

Chieftain Armoured Recovery Vehicle (FV 4202): Prototype built in 1971, now in production. It is armed with a 7.62mm machine gun (cupola mounted) and 12 smoke dischargers. It has a crew of four. The vehicle has two winches, each of the double capstan type to give sustained pulls to the front of the vehicle of 30 tonnes and 3 tonnes respectively. A hydraulic operated dozer bla ▸ is fitted at the front of the vehicle. Basic data is as follows:

Length: 8.256m
Width: 3.518m (over blade)
Height: 2.746m
Fuel: 955 litres

Weight: 52,000kg (loaded) 50,250kg (empty)
Speed: 41.5km/ph (road)
Range: 322km (road)

Chieftain Bridgelayer (FV 4205): This is a Chieftain chassis fitted with a 24.40m long class 60 scissors bridge. This can cover a span of 22.9m, a 13.4m bridge has been developed. This bridge is launched hydraulically and takes about three minutes to lay in position. The vehicle has a crew of three men. Basic data is as follows:

Length: 13.73m
Width: 4.16m
Height: 3.93m
Weight: 53,300kg

Chieftain Armoured Vehicle Royal Engineers (FV 4203): This was a project only. It is not in service.

Employment
Chieftains have now replaced all Centurion gun tanks in the British Army. Chieftains are also in service with the Iranian Army and on order for Kuwait. The AVLB and ARV are also now in service with the British Army.

Vickers MBT Mk 1 Main Battle Tank   Great Britain

Armament: 1 × 105mm L7A1 gun, elevation + 20°, depression − 7°
1 × 12.7mm ranging machine gun
1 × 7.62mm co-axial machine gun
1 × 7.62mm anti-aircraft machine gun
2 × 6 barrelled smoke dischargers
44 rounds of 105mm ammunition (50)
600 rounds of 12.7mm ammunition
3000 rounds of 7.62mm ammunition

Crew: 4

Length: 9.728m (gun forward) (9.788m) 7.920m (hull only) (7.561m)

Width: 3.168m

Height: 2.640m (w/o A/A machine gun) (2.887m)
2.438m (turret roof)

G/Clearance: .406m

Weight: 38,600kg (loaded) (39,100kg) 36,000kg (empty) (36,400kg)

G/Pressure: .90kg.cm^2

Engine: Leyland L60 Mk 4B, 6 cylinder, water-cooled multi-fuel engine developing 650bhp at 2670 rpm
(General Motors 12V 71T turbo-charged diesel, developing 800bhp at 2500rpm)

Speed: 56km/ph (road)
Range: 480km (road)
Fuel: 1000 litres
Fording: 1.143m
V/Obstacle: .914m
Trench: 2.43♥m
Gradient: 60%
Armour: 25mm−80mm (estimate)
Data in brackets relates to Mk 3 where different.

Development
In August 1961 an agreement was signed between Vickers Limited and the Indian Government. Under this agreement Vickers undertook to design an MBT and also set up a production line in India; some tanks were also to be built in Britain. The first prototype was completed early in 1963. The tank uses the engine and transmission of the Chieftain, gun of the late Centurion (also used in the Leopard, Pz 61 and so on), and a suspension based on the cancelled FV 300 series. Production commenced at Vickers Elswick works in 1964 and the first British-built tank was delivered to India in 1965. In the meantime a factory was built at Avadi, near Madras, and the first Indian-built tank was completed in 1966. Early Indian tanks used many components from the UK. The Vickers MBT is called VIJAYANTA by the Indians. According to reports from India, 66 had been built by mid-1968 and 300 by 1971, the production target being 200 tanks a year.

The tank is fitted with a gun control and stabilisation system developed by GEC-AEI. This enables the tank to fire on the move.

The vehicle can be fitted with a flotation screen. This takes about 15-20 minutes to be erected and enables the vehicle to cross rivers, being propelled by its tracks at about 6km/ph. Other optional equipment includes an NBC system and infra-red driving and fighting equipment.

Vickers MBT Mk 3

Variants
Mk 2: This was a project only and was basically a Mk 1 with two BAC Swingfire ATGW missiles mounted either side of the turret rear.

Mk 3: The improvements over the Mk 1 include a new turret and mantlet, gun has a depression of − 10°, new and improved glacis plate, increased ammunition stowage (50 rounds), it can also be fitted with passive night fighting and night driving equipment. The FCS incorporates a laser rangefinder in the gunner's sight, this is linked to the commander's sight. The armament is stabilised in azimuth and elevation by an all electric gun control equipment.

Employment
The Vickers MBT Mk 1 is in service with India and Kuwait.

Centurion Main Battle Tank   Great Britain

Armament: 1 × 105mm L7A2 gun, elevation + 20°, depression − 10°
1 × 12.7mm ranging machine gun
1 × 7.62mm co-axial machine gun
1 × 7.62mm anti-aircraft machine gun
2 × 6 barrelled smoke dischargers
64 rounds of 105mm ammunition
600 rounds of 12.7mm ammunition
4750 rounds of 7.62mm ammunition
Crew: 4
Length: 9.854m (including gun)
7.823m (excluding gun)
Width: 3.39m
Height: 3.009m (w/o A/A machine gun)
G/Clearance: .51m
Weight: 51,820kg (loaded)
G/Pressure: .95kg.cm²
Engine: Rolls-Royce Meteor Mk 1VB, 12 cylinder, liquid cooled petrol engine developing 650bhp at 2550rpm
Speed: 34.6km/ph (road)
Range: 190km (road)
Fuel: 1037 litres
Fording: 1.45m
2.74m (with kit)
V/Obstacle: .914m
Trench: 3.352m
Gradient: 60%
Armour: 17mm−152mm
Note. *The above data relates to the Mk 13 Centurion.*

Development
The Centurion was developed during World War II as a cruiser tank. The first prototype was completed in 1945. This was called the A-41. Later this was changed to Centurion Mk 1. AEC were the original design parents. First production vehicles were the Mk 2s which entered service after the end of the war. Centurions were built by Vickers, Leyland Motors and the ROF at Leeds. The Centurion chassis has been used as a basis for many prototype vehicles including the FV 4004 Conway, FV 4005 Tank Destroyer, FV 4019 Flame-thrower, FV 3802 25 pounder and FV 3805 5.5in self-propelled guns. The British Aircraft Corporation (GW Division) did have a project to fit Swingfire ATGW to the vehicle, but this only reached mock-up stage. Centurions can be fitted with a dozer blade on the front of the vehicle. A summary of Centurion tanks still in service is listed below.

Variants
Mk 3: 20 pounder (83.4mm) gun with 65 rounds, 7.92mm Besa co-axial machine gun, Meteor Mk 1VB engine. Most were re-built to Mk 5 standards.

Mk 5: Based on Mk 3 hull but with 7.62mm co-axial machine gun. Vickers were design parents. Could tow a trailer with additional fuel.

Mk 5/1: Is Mk 5 up armoured, designated FV 4011.

Mk 5/2: Is Mk 5 up gunned with 105mm gun.

Mk 6: Is Mk 5 up gunned and up

armoured, also has additional fuel in hull rear.

Mk 6/1: Is Mk 6 with infra-red driving and fighting equipment, stowage basket on rear of turret.

Mk 6/2: Is Mk 6 with 12.7mm ranging machine gun for 105mm gun.

Mk 7: in Designated FV 4007, design parents were Leyland Motors. Armament is a 20 pounder gun with 61 rounds, 7.62mm co-axial machine gun, fume extractor on barrel, additional fuel.

Mk 7/1: Is Mk 7 up armoured, designated FV 4012.

Mk 7/2: Is Mk 7 up gunned with 105mm gun.

Mk 8: Based on Mk 7 hull, 20 pounder gun with 63 ready rounds, fume extractor on barrel. Meteor 1VC engine, contra-rotating cupola with raisable roof for commander, resilient gun mantlet. New elevating gear.

Mk 8/1: Is Mk 8 up armoured.

Mk 8/2: Is Mk 8 up gunned with 105mm gun.

Mk 9: Is Mk 7 up gunned and up armoured, designated FV 4015.

Mk 9/1: Is Mk 9 with infra-red driving and fighting equipment, stowage basket on rear of the turret.

Mk 9/2: Is Mk 9 with ranging machine gun for 105mm gun.

Mk 10: Is Mk 8 up gunned and up armoured, designated FV 4017. Armed with 105mm L7A1 gun with 70 rounds, new control equipment for gun, impact resisting trunions, automatic stabilisation when vehicle exceeds 6.43km/ph.

Mk 10/1: Is Mk 10 with infra-red driving and fighting equipment and stowage basket on rear of turret.

Mk 10/2: Is Mk 10 with ranging machine gun for 105mm gun.

Mk 11: Is Mk 6 with ranging machine gun, infra-red driving and fighting equipment and a stowage basket on the rear of the turret.

Mk 12: Is Mk 9 with infra-red driving and fighting equipment, ranging machine gun and stowage basket on the rear of the turret.

Mk 13: Is Mk 10 with ranging machine gun and infra-red driving and fighting equipment.

Vickers Modified Centurions (1973): In May 1973 Vickers Limited demonstrated a Centurion MBT which had been fitted with a new powerpack based on a GM 12V-71T diesel engine with a power output of 720bhp and a new gun control and stabilisation system. Under development is a laser range-finder, new cupola, passive nightfighting equipment, revised ventilation system and new final drives. Thus resulting in a highly effective MBT at low outlay. This vehicle also has a larger radius of action and a higher maximum speed. Two have been delivered to Switzerland.

Armoured Recovery Vehicle, Centurion Mk 2 (FV 4006): This is a Mk 3 Centurion with an armoured super-structure, its equipment includes a winch (maximum capacity 90,000kg pro rata), spades at the rear, jib crane, tools and so on. Armament is a 7.62mm machine gun and smoke dischargers.

Length: 8.96m
Width: 3.39m
Height: 2.88m
Weight: 50,200kg (loaded)
47,250kg (empty)
Crew: 4

Centurion Mk 5/2 of Dutch Army

Centurion Mk. 2 ARV of Swiss Army

Centurion Bridgelayer

Tank, Beach, ARV, Centurion (BARV) (FV 4018): This is basically a Centurion with no turret and fitted with a super-structure. It is capable of operating in 2.74m of water.
Length: 8.08m
Width: 3.39m
Height: 3.45m
Weight: 40,500kg (loaded)
37,800kg (empty)
Crew: 4
Tank, Armoured Vehicle, Royal Engineers (AVRE) Mk 5 (FV 4003): This is armed with a 165mm demolition charge projector as well as a co-axial machine gun. At the front of the vehicle is a hydraulically operated dozer blade and it can also carry a fascine. It can tow a trailer fitted with the Giant Viper mine clearance equipment.
Length: 8.70m (including blade)
Width: 3.39m (without blade)
3.95m (with blade)
Height: 2.50m
Weight: 51,800kg (loaded)
49,500kg (empty)
Tank, Bridgelayer, Centurion Mk 5 (FV 4002): This is fitted with a single span bridge that can be laid across gaps up to 13.72m wide, this takes only two minutes to lay. Data of the vehicle with bridge is:

Length: 16.3m
Width: 4.26m
Height: 3.88m
Weight: 50,485kg (loaded)
48,700kg (empty)
Crew: 2–3
Tank ARK Centurion Mk 5 (FV 4016): This is used for spanning gaps up to 22.86m wide. The vehicle itself enters the ditch and then opens out. Data with the trackways in travelling position is:
Length: 10.37m
Width: 3.96m
Height: 3.88m
Weight: 51,800kg (loaded)
Employment
Australia: Centurion Mk 5 and Mk 7 (some with 105mm guns, Mk 5s have ranging machine gun for 20 pounder), ARV Mk 2 Bridgelayer Mk 5. (Being replaced by Leopards.)
Canada: Centurion Mk 2, Mk 5, Mk 5/2 and ARV Mk 2. (Being replaced by Leopards.)
Denmark: Centurions with 20 pounders, 105mm, ARV Mk 2. Centurion MBTs have German-built AEG dual purpose IR/White Light searchlight type XSW 30U (E) and IR sighting device B8V (ELTRO).
Egypt: Has a few Mk 3s, doubtful if still in service.
Great Britain: Last MBTs phased out

65

1973, all Mks still in use for training, plus ARVs, bridgelayers and AVREs.
India: Centurion Mk 5 and Mk 7.
Iraq: Centurion Mk 5.
Israel: various Mks. including ARV Mk 2. See Israel section.
Jordan: Centurion Mk 5 and Mk 10.
Lebanon: Centurion Mk 5.
Libya: Has a few Centurion Mk 5s, probably non-operational.
Netherlands: Centurion Mk 5, Mk 5/2, Mk5 with special dozer, Mk 5 with scissors bridge, ARV Mk 2.
Kuwait: Centurion Mk 5 and Mk 10.

South Africa: Mk 5 and Mk 7.
Sweden: Mk 3 and Mk 5 (originally called Strv 81, when up gunned to 105mm = Strv 102), Mk 10 is Strv 101, ARV Mk 2 is Bgbv 81, monowheel fuel trailers used, Strv 101 and Strv 102 have new radios and 7.62mm machine guns. A major refit programme is scheduled for 1979–82.
Switzerland: Centurion Mk 3 (Pz 55), Mk 5 (Pz 60), Mk 7 (Pz 57), ARV Mk 2 (Entpannungspanzer 56), some MBT have 105mm guns.

Charioteer Tank Destroyer   Great Britain

Armament: 1 × 84mm gun, elevation + 10°, depression − 5°
1 × 7.62mm co-axial machine gun
2 × 6 barrelled smoke dischargers
25 rounds of 84mm ammmunition
3375 rounds of 7.62mm ammunition
Crew: 4
Length: 8.839m (including gun)
6.425m (excluding gun)
Width: 3.067m
Height: 2.59m
G/Clearance: .406m
Weight: 28,958kg
G/Pressure: .98kg.cm²
Engine: Rolls-Royce Meteor Mk 3, 12 cylinder (V-12), water-cooled petrol engine developing 600hp at 2550rpm

Speed: 51.5km/ph (road)
Range: 241km (road)
Fuel: 526 litres
Fording: 1.04m
V/Obstacle: .914m
Trench: 2.362m
Gradient: 40%
Armour: 10mm–64mm
Development/Employment
In 1952/1954 a large number of Cromwells were modified by fitting a new turret, mounting the 84mm gun as used in the Centurion. The hull machine gun was removed and there were a number of other modifications. This tank then became the Charioteer. The vehicle is still used by Finland and the Lebanon.

Churchill Infantry Tank   Great Britain

A small quantity of these are still used by Eire and there are unconfirmed reports that there are some in Iraq and India. Also unconfirmed are reports of Valentines in the Sudan and Portugal.

Comet Cruiser Tank   Great Britain

Armament: 1 × 77mm gun, elevation + 20° depression − 12°
1 × 7.92mm co-axial machine gun
1 × 7.92mm bow mounted machine gun
2 × 6 barrelled smoke dischargers
61 rounds of 77mm ammunition
5175 rounds of 7.92mm ammunition
Crew: 5
Length: 7.66m (including gun)
6.55m (excluding gun)
Width: 3.073m
Height: 2.67m
G/Clearance: .46m
Weight: 33,250kg
G/Pressure: .97kg.cm²
Engine: Rolls-Royce Meteor Mk 3, 12 cylinder (V-12), water-cooled petrol engine developing 600hp at 2500rpm

Speed: 51.5km/ph (road)
Range: 241km (road)
Fuel: 527 litres
Fording: 1.04m
V/Obstacle: .914m
Trench: 2.438m
Gradient: 60%
Armour: 14mm–101mm

Development/Employment
The Comet was a complete re-design of the Cromwell tank. This was undertaken by Leyland Motors in 1943/1944. The vehicle saw action in the closing months of World War II and postwar in Korea. The vehicle is still used by a number of countries including Burma, Eire, Finland and South Africa.

A Comet Tank

FV 601 Alvis Saladin Mk 2
Armoured Car

Great Britain

Armament: 1 × 76mm gun, elevation +20°, depression −10°, 43 rounds of ammunition carried
1 × 7.62mm machine gun co-axial with main armament
1 × 7.62mm machine gun for commander (A/A role)
2 × 6 barrelled smoke dischargers
2750 rounds of 7.62mm ammunition are carried
Crew: 3
Length: 5.284m (including gun)
4.93m (excluding gun)
Width: 2.54m
Height: 2.39m (w/o machine gun)
G/Clearance: .426m
Weight: 11,590kg (loaded)
10,500kg (empty)
G/Pressure: 1.12kg.cm^2
Engine: Rolls-Royce B.80 Mk 6A, 8 cylinder petrol engine developing 170hp at 3750rpm
Speed: 72km/ph (road)
Range: 400km (road)

Fuel: 241 litres
Fording: 1.07m
2.13m (with kit)
V/Obstacle: .46m
Trench: 1.52m
Gradient: 42%
Armour: 8mm–32mm

Development
Design of the Saladin dates to 1947 but it was not until 1954 that the prototype vehicle was completed, the first production models followed in 1958, production of the Saladin was completed in 1972. Production being undertaken by Alvis Limited of Coventry.
The Saladin uses many components of the FV 603 Saracen APC, one of the differences being that the Saracen has its engine in the front, and the Saladin has its engine in the rear.

Below: Alvis Saladin FV 601

Variants

The production vehicle was the Mk 2, its full designation being FV 601(C) Armoured Car 76mm (Alvis Saladin Mk 2 6 x 6). BAC and Alvis modified a Saladin to carry a single Swingfire anti-tank missile either side of the turret and two reserve missiles at the rear of the vehicle. This, however, was a project only. Also tested in 1966 was a Saladin fitted with a flotation screen, this enabled the vehicle to cross rivers, being propelled in the water by its wheels. It did not progress further than trials. The German Border Police use the FV 601(D). This has no co-axial machine gun and has German type lights and six German smoke grenade launchers either side of the turret. Its German designation is SW-111 Kfz-93, Geschützer Sonderwagen 111.

Employment

Used by Abu Dhabi, Bahrain, Great Britain (being replaced by Scorpion), German Border Police, Ghana, Indonesia, Jordan, Kuwait, Libya, Muscat and Oman, Nigeria, Qatar, South Yemen, Sudan, Tunisia, Uganda, Ceylon, Kenya, and Portugal. Production has now been completed.

Other British Armoured Cars Still in Service

Daimler: Still used by some countries including India.

AEC: Still used by the Lebanon.

Humber: Still used by Burma, Ceylon, Cyprus, India, Mexico.

Dingo: The Daimler scout car is still used by Cyprus and Portugal.

Scorpion Family   Great Britain
Combat Vehicle (Reconnaissance) Tracked

	FV 101	FV 102	FV 103	FV 104	FV 105	FV 106	FV 107
Crew:	3	3	3 + 4	3 + 4	5/6	3	3
Length:	4.388m	4.759m	4.839m	4.991m	4.991m	4.934m	4.388m
Width:	2.184m	2.184m	2.184m	2.184m	2.184m	2.184m	2.184m
Height:	2.096m	2.210m	2.250m	2.016m	2.016m	2.023m	2.115m
G/Clearance:	.356m	.356m	.356m	.356m	.356m	.356m	.356m
Weight							
Loaded:	7960kg	8221kg	8172kg	7710kg	7918kg	8002kg	7900kg
G/Pressure:	.35kg.cm^2	.35kg.cm^2	.35kg.cm^2	.35kg.cm^2	.35kg.cm^2	.35kg.cm^2	.35kg.cm^2
Speed Road:	87km/ph	87km/ph	87km/ph	87km/ph	87km/ph	87km/ph	87km/ph
Range Road:	644km	644km	644km	644km	644km	644km	644km
Fuel:	391 litres	364 litres	364 litres	364 litres	364 litres	364 litres	391 litres
Fording:	1.07m	1.07m	1.07m	1.07m	1.07m	1.07m	1.07m
V/Obstacle:	.508m	.508m	.508m	.508m	.508m	.508m	.508m
Trench:	2.057m	2.057m	2.057m	2.057m	2.057m	2.057m	2.057m
Gradient:	70%	70%	70%	70%	70%	70%	70%
Engine:	All are powered by Jaguar 6 cylinder water-cooled petrol engine developing 195bhp at 4750rpm						

Development

The Scorpion was preceded by a vehicle known as the TV 15000 and a Mobile Test Rig (MTR). In September 1967, Alvis of Coventry was awarded a contract to build the prototype Scorpions. The first prototype was completed in January 1969, and in September 1969, prototypes were shown to the public and Press. The first production order was awarded to Alvis in May 1970, and the vehicle entered production in 1971, the first production Scorpion being completed early in 1972. In 1970 a co-production order was signed between Great Britain and Belgium, Belgium will receive a total of 700 members of the Scorpion family.

The basic role of the Scorpion is that of reconnaissance and for this reason the vehicle is equipped with a complete range of day and night observation, driving and fighting systems. An NBC system is fitted. The vehicle can be made amphibious in several minutes by erecting a flotation screen around the top of the hull, the vehicle is propelled in the water by its tracks at 6.5km/ph. A propeller kit is under development and this will increase the vehicle's water speed to 9.6km/ph. The Scorpion is of all welded aluminium armour construction and uses the same engine as the Fox CVR(W). Scorpion can also be fitted with the ZB 298 Radar System, Radiac system and navigational aids. The vehicle is air-portable by such aircraft as the C-130 (2 vehicles) or CH-53A helicopter.

Variants

FV 101 Scorpion: This is armed with a

FV 101
Scorpion, Combat
Vehicle Reconnaissance
(Tracked)

FV 102 Striker,
Anti-Tank Guided
Weapon Vehicle.
A Swingfire Launching ATGW

76mm gun with an elevation of + 35° and a depression of − 10°, a 7.62mm machine gun is fitted and this can also be used as a ranging gun, 2 three barreled smoke dischargers are fitted. Forty rounds of 76mm and 3000 rounds of 7.62mm ammunition are carried.

FV 102 Striker: This is an anti-tank guided weapons vehicle. Mounted on the top of the hull, towards the rear is a launching bin containing five BAC Swingfire ATGW with a range of 4000m, a further five missiles are carried inside of the vehicle. A 7.62mm machine gun is cupola mounted and smoke dischargers are mounted on the front of the vehicle.

FV 103 Spartan: This is a small armoured personnel carrier and would be used to carry assault troops or engineers. It could also be used to support other members of the family for example carrying spare missiles or ammunition. It is armed with a cupola mounted 7.62mm machine gun and smoke dischargers. Alvis have suggested that this can be armed with the Hughes TOW missile system.

FV 104 Samaritan: This is an ambulance and has a raised roof, no armament is fitted. It can carry four stretcher patients, six sitting patients or three sitting and two stretchers, in addition to its crew.

FV 105 Sultan: This is a command vehicle and has a similar hull to that of the FV 104. Additional radios are fitted as are mapboards. A penthouse can be erected at the rear of the vehicle to give additional working space. It is armed with a pintle mounted 7.62mm machine gun.

FV 106 Samson: This is a recovery vehicle and has an internally mounted winch with a capacity of 20,000kg and 229m of wire rope. This is driven from the main engine and has a variable speed. Anchors are provided at the rear of the vehicle.

FV 107 Scimitar: This has the same hull and turret as the Scorpion but it is armed with a 30mm Rarden cannon and a 7.62mm machine gun. The gun has an elevation of + 35° and a depression of − 10°. One sixty-five rounds of 30mm and 3000 rounds of 7.62mm ammunition are carried. Two three-barrelled smoke dischargers are fitted either side of the turret front.

Employment
In service with Abu Dhabi, Belgium Great Britain, Iran, Nigeria, and Saudi-Arabia.

69

FV 107 Scimitar is armed with a 30mm Rarden cannon, as fitted to the Fox Armoured Car

Fox
Combat Vehicle Reconnaissance (Wheeled)

Great Britain

Armament: 1 × 30mm Rarden cannon, elevation + 41°, depression − 14°
1 × 7.62mm machine gun co-axial with main armament.
2 × 4 barrelled smoke dischargers
96 rounds of 30mm ammunition in clips of 3, 2600 rounds of 7.62mm ammunition
Crew: 3
Length: 5.359m (gun forward)
4.242m (hull)
Width: 2.134m
Height: 2.20m (overall)
1.98m (turret top)
G/Clearance: .30m
Weight: 6386kg (loaded)
5733kg (empty)
G/Pressure: .46kg.cm²
Engine: Jaguar 4.2 litre, 6 cylinder petrol engine developing 195hp at 5000rpm
Speed: 104km/ph (road)
5km/ph (water)
Range: 434km (road)
Fuel: 145 litres
Fording: 1.01m
V/Obstacle: .50m
Trench: 1.22m (with channels)

Gradient: 50%
Track: 1.753m
Wheelbase: 2.464m

Development
The Fox is the development of the Ferret scout car. Design work on the Fox (FV 721) started in 1965/1966. Prototypes were built by the Daimler Company at Radford, Coventry, the first prototype being completed in November 1967. The vehicle was first shown to the public in October 1969. The production contract was awarded to the Royal Ordnance Factory at Leeds and the first production vehicle was completed in May 1973.
A flotation screen is carried around the top of the hull. This can be quickly erected and enables the vehicle to cross streams and rivers. The vehicle is propelled in the water by its wheels at about 5km/ph.
The hull and turret of the Fox are constructed of welded aluminium armour. Equipment includes an NBC system, navigation system and a full range of day and night vision and fire control devices. The engine

CVR(W) Fox

70

of the Fox is also used in the CVR(T) Scorpion and the 30mm Rarden cannon is also used in the Scimitar vehicle. This 30mm cannon can fire a British developed APDS round or standard Hispano HE, AP or Practice rounds. Rate of fire is 90 rounds per minute, and maximum range is about 4000m. Single shots or bursts can be fired and the spent ammunition cases are ejected outside the vehicle.

The ZB 298 Radar System can be fitted to the vehicle if required.

Variants

The FV 722 Vixen, Combat Vehicle Reconnaissance (Wheeled) Liason was cancelled in the December 1974 defence cuts.

Employment

Fox is in service with Great Britain, Iran, Nigeria, Saudi-Arabia, and Kenya.

Ferret Family Light Scout Cars Great Britain

	Mk 1/1 FV 701	Mk 1/2 FV 704	Mk 2/3 FV 701	Mk 2/6 FV 703	Mk 4 FV 711	Mk 5 FV 712
Crew:	2–3	3	2	2	2–3	2
Length:	3.84m	3.84m	3.84m	3.84m	3.96m	3.96m
Width:	1.91m	1.91m	1.91m	1.91m	2.13m	2.13m
Height:	1.45m	1.65m	1.88m	1.88m	2.03m	2.08m
G/Clearance:	.33m	.33m	.33m	.33m	.41m	.41m
Weight Loaded:	4210kg	4370kg	4395kg	4560kg	5400kg	5890kg
Weight Empty:	3510kg	3660kg	3684kg	3680kg	4725kg	4980kg
Speed Road:	93km/ph	93km/ph	93km/ph	93km/ph	80km/ph	80km/ph
Range Road:	300km	300km	300km	300km	300km	300km
Fuel:	96 litres	96 litres	96 litres	96 litres	96 litres	96 litres
Fording (w/o kit):	.914m	.914m	.914m	.914m	.914m	.914m
V/Obstacle:	.406m	.406m	.406m	.406m	.406m	.406m
Trench (with channels):	1.22m	1.22m	1.22m	1.22m	1.22m	1.22m
Gradient:	46%	46%	46%	46%	46%	46%
Wheelbase:	2.286m	2.286m	2.286m	2.286m	2.286m	2.286m
Track:	1.55m	1.55m	1.55m	1.55m	1.75m	1.75m
Engine:	All have Rolls-Royce B60 Mk 6A 6 cylinder, water-cooled petrol engine developing 129bhp at 3750rpm					

Development

Development started shortly after the end of World War II. The first prototype, the Mk 1, was completed by Daimler in 1949 and delivered in 1950. Production was undertaken by Daimler at Coventry and the first production vehicle was completed in 1952. Production continued until 1971. The Ferret was further developed into the Fox.

The hull of the Ferret is of all welded construction, armour thickness is 6mm–16mm. The vehicle does not have an NBC system. All Ferrets have two 3-barrelled smoke dischargers.

Variants

Mk 1/1 FV 701 (J) Scout Car Liaison: This is the basic open topped version and is armed with a Bren LMG or a 7.62mm machine gun. A trials version existed with a flotation screen.

Mk 1/2 (FV 704) Scout Car Liaison: This is a Mk 1/1 with a small turret with a flat roof and it is armed with a Bren LMG.

Mk 2/2: This is a Mk 2 with an extension collar between the top of the vehicle and the machine-gun turret. The Mk 2 has a 2-door machine gun turret and the Mk 2/1 is a Mk 1 with a 2-door machine-gun turret.

Mk 2/3 FV 701 (H) Scout Car Reconnaissance: This is similar to the Mk 1/1 except that it has a 7.62mm machine gun in a turret with an elevation of +45° and a depression of −15°, traverse being 360°. Two thousand five hundred rounds of 7.62mm ammunition are carried. This vehicle can also be fitted with the ZB 298 Radar System. The Ferret Mk 2/4 and Mk 2/5 have additional armour.

Mk 2/6 FV 703 Scout Car Reconnaissance (Guided Weapon): This is the Mk 2/3 but with a VIGILANT wire guided anti-tank missile mounted either side of the turret with a common elevating mechanism. Two spare missiles are carried in place of the spare wheel. The missiles can be controlled from within the vehicle or away from the vehicle with the aid of a combined sight/controller and separation cable. The missiles have a range of 200m to 1375m.

Mk 2/7: This is a Mk 2/6 but with its missile equipment removed and used as a reconnaissance vehicle.

Mk 3 Scout Car Liaison: This is a Mk 1/1 but with modified suspension, larger wheels and a flotation screen.

Mk 4 FV 711 Scout Car Reconnaissance: This is a re-built Mk 2 and has stronger suspension units, disc brakes, larger wheels and tyres. A flotation screen can be quickly erected and the vehicle is propelled in the water by its wheels at a maximum speed of 3.8km/ph.

Mk 5 FV 712 Scout Car Reconnaissance/Guided Weapon: Only a small number of these were built and they were re-builds of earlier vehicles. It has a turret with a 7.62mm machine gun and two launcher boxes (elevated to fire), each containing two BAC Swingfire ATGW. A further two missiles are carried under armour. The missiles can be fired from within the vehicle or away from the vehicle.

Employment
In service with Abu Dhabi, Bahrain, Brunei, Burma, Cameroon, Canada, Ceylon, Gambia, Ghana, Great Britain, Iran, Indonesia, Iraq, Jamaica, Jordan, Kenya, Kuwait, Libya, Malaysia, Muscat and Oman, New Zealand, Nigeria, Qatar, Ras Al Khaimah, Rhodesia, Sierra Leone, Somali, South Africa, South Arabia, South Yemen, Sudan, Uganda, Zaire, Zambia, France, Malagasy, Malawi and Upper Volta.

Above: *Mk 1/1 modified for use in Northern Ireland*

Ferret Mk 2/6 firing a BAC Vigilant Anti-Tank Guided Missile

Shorland Mk 3 Armoured Patrol Car   Great Britain

Armament: 1 x 7.62mm machine gun and 1500 rounds of ammunition
2 x 3 smoke dischargers (optional)
Crew: 3
Length: 4.597m
Width: 1.778m
Height: 2.286m
G/Clearance: .21m (minimum)
Weight: 3360kg (loaded)
2931kg (empty)
G/Pressure: 2.4kg.cm²
Engine: Rover 6 cylinder petrol engine developing 91bhp at 4500rpm. 2.625 litres
Speed: 88.4km/ph (road)
Range: 257km (standard tank)
514km (long range tank)
Fuel: 64 litres (standard)
128 litres (long range)
V/Obstacle: .23m
Trench: not applicable
Armour: 8.25mm–11mm

Development

The Shorland was conceived, prototype built, and placed in production in 1965. It was designed by the General Engineering Division of Short Brothers and Harland, at their Newtownards factory. The vehicle is essentially a 2.77m modified Land Rover chassis with an armoured body, in addition the engine and radiator have been armoured. The Shorland was first used by the Royal Ulster Constabulary, since then however the British Army have taken over the vehicles. Shorland is recognised by the British Army as an Internal Security Vehicle.

Variants

The first model to enter production was the Mk 1. This had hull armour of 7.25mm and was powered by a 4 cylinder Rover petrol engine developing 67bhp at 4100rpm. This was followed by the Mk 2 which had a 4 cylinder petrol engine developing 77bhp at 4100rpm.
The latest production model is the Mk 3. This has a thicker hull armour of 8.25mm which is resistant to the standard 7.62mm NATO round, also it is powered by a 6 cylinder petrol engine developing 95bhp at 4500rpm.
Other variants have included a Shorland with two Vigilant ATGW, Shorland with water cannon, Shorland with tear gas projector and the Shorland Security Vehicle for carrying cash and bullion. A more recent version is the SB 301 armoured personnel carrier. There is a separate entry for this vehicle.

Employment

To date over 400 Shorlands have been built and the vehicle is in service with 22 countries including Argentina, Brunei, Great Britain, Libya, Persian Gulf States, and Thailand.

Shorland Armoured Patrol Car armed with smoke dischargers

FV 432 Series
Armoured Personnel Carrier

Great Britain

Armament: 1 × 7.62mm GPMG and 2 × 3 barrelled smoke dischargers
Crew: 2 + 10
Length: 5.251m (overall)
4.87m (hull)
Width: 2.80m (overall)
Height: 2.286m (including machine gun)
1.879m (hull roof)
G /Clearance: .406m
Weight: 15,280kg (loaded)
13,740kg (empty)
G /Pressure: .78kg.cm^2
Engine: Rolls-Royce K60 No 4 Mk 4F, multi-fuel, 240bhp at 3750rpm
Speed: 52km /ph (road)
6.6km /ph (water)
Range: 580km (road)
Fuel: 454 litres
Fording: Amphibious
V /Obstacle: .609m
Trench: 2.05m
Gradient: 60%
Armour: 6mm–12mm

Development
The FV 432 was developed from the earlier FV 420 series. The first prototype FV 432 was completed in 1961 and production commenced in 1963. Production was undertaken by Joseph Sankey and has now been completed. Prototype FV 432s were powered by a B.81 petrol engine and were called Trojans. First production FV 432s were the Mk 1 and Mk 1 /1, followed by the Mk 2 and Mk 2 /1. The FV 432 is made amphibious by erecting a screen and is propelled in the water by its tracks. It is fitted with an NBC system and has infrared driving lights. The FV 433 Abbot uses components of the FV 432.

Variants
The FV 432 can be adopted for the following roles:
(a) **Mortar:** 81mm mortar with a traverse of 360°, 160 rounds of ammunition, crew of six, laden weight 16,400kg.
(b) **Command:** Has mapboards, additional radios. Crew of seven, laden weight 15,500kg. A large tent can be erected at the rear of the vehicle to give additional working space.
(c) **Recovery:** Fitted with a winch, winch sub-frame, earth anchor, 107m of cable, maximum line pull 2 part tackle 16,270kg. Winch is driven from the PTO on the engine transfer case.
(d) **Wombat:** Can be fired mounted or dismounted, 14 rounds of ammunition are carried, crew of four, weight 15,870kg.
(e) **Load Carrier:** Can carry 3670kg of cargo.
(f) **Minelayer:** Can tow the Bar minelaying equipment and can be fitted with the Ranger anti-personnel minelayer system.

FV 432 of the Scots Guards

The FV 438 launching a BAC Swingfire ATGW

FV 432 fitted with the turret mounted 7.62mm GPMG

(g) **Ambulance:** Can carry four stretchers (two each side), or two stretchers on one side and five seated patients on the other side. Crew of two.

(h) **Carl Gustav:** Bar across fighting compartment on which is mounted a Carl Gustav anti-tank weapon.

(i) **Artillery Control:** Fitted with the FACE (Field Artillery Computer Equipment).

(j) **Radar:** Can be fitted with the ZB 298 ground surveillance radar.

(k) **Navigation:** Can be fitted with navigation equipment.

(l) Fitted with the Cymbeline Mortar locating system.

(m) Fitted with a turret mounted 7.62mm MG.

(n) Fitted with twin 7.62mm GPMG in place of single GPMG.

(o) Fitted with turret mounted Rarden 30mm gun. It would appear that this will not now be entering service.

The following use a modified FV 432 hull: FV 434 Carrier, Maintenance, Full Tracked: This version is fitted with an HIAB crane and carries special tools and equipment. Crew is four, data as for FV 432 except:

Length: 5.72m

Weight: 17,750kg (loaded)
15,040kg (empty)
Height: 2.83m (travelling)
Width: 2.84m
Its crane can lift 1250kg at 3.96m radius to 3050kg at 2.26m radius.

FV 436 Self-Propelled Mortar Locating Radar: The rear hull has been cut away to provide a mounting for the Green Archer Mortar Locating Radar. Crew of three and it retains its amphibious capability.

FV 437 Pathfinder Recovery Vehicle (Trials only): This is a much modified FV 432 whose job was to recover vehicles in water.

FV 438 Swingfire Launcher Vehicle: This version has two launcher boxes for the Swingfire ATGW. A total of 14 missiles are carried. It also carries a 7.62mm GPMG. It has a crew of three. Data is similar to the basic FV 432 except:

Height: 2.705m
Weight: 16,200kg (loaded)
14,520kg (empty)
Sonic Detection Vehicle: This is used by the Royal Artillery to locate enemy gun and mortar positions.

Employment
Used only by the British Army.

75

FV 603 Alvis Saracen

Armoured Personnel Carrier

Great Britain

Armament: 1 × 7.62mm machine gun, elevation + 45°, depression − 15°
1 × 7.62mm machine gun on ring mount at rear of vehicle
2 × 3 barrelled smoke dischargers
3000 rounds of 7.62mm machine gun ammunition
Crew: 2 + 10
Length: 5.233m (overall)
Width: 2.539m
Height: 2.463m
G /Clearance: .432m
Weight: 10,170kg (loaded)
8640kg (empty)
G /Pressure: .98kg.cm²
Engine: Rolls-Royce B.80 Mk 6A, 8 cylinder petrol engine developing 170hp at 3750rpm
Speed: 72km /ph (road)
Range: 400km
Fuel: 200 litres
Fording: 1.07m
1.98m (with kit)
V /Obstacle: .46m
Trench: 1.52m
Gradient: 42%
Armour: 8mm–16mm

Development

Design work on the Saracen started shortly after the end of World War II. The first prototype was built in 1950, followed by the first production vehicle in 1952. The last Saracen was built in 1972. The Saracen uses many components of the Saladin armoured car and the Stalwart High Mobility Load Carrier.

Variants

The full designation of the Saracen is Carrier Personnel Wheeled APC Mk 2 (Alvis Saracen 6 × 6). The Mk 1 had a slightly different turret and other minor differences. The basic vehicle can be quickly adopted for use as an ambulance, load carrier or engineer vehicle. The FV 603(C) incorporates reverse flow cooling enabling the vehicle to operate in the Middle East. This is distinguishable from the basic vehicle by its different arrangement of engine covers and the large cover over the radiator.

FV 604 Command Post: This is a Saracen without its turret, modified to carry additional radios, extra batteries, auxiliary charging equipment, map boards, the seating arrangements have also been modified. Sometimes an LMG is fitted on a ring mount slightly forward to where the turret was. Some FV 603s have been converted to FV 604 standards but retaining their turrets.

FV 610 Command Post: This is similar to the FV 604 but its height has been increased to 2.36m as this is intended to be used in the static role for longer periods. Additional working space is obtained by erecting tentage at the rear of the vehicle

FV 603 Saracen Armoured Personnel Carrier

(FV 604 is similar). This vehicle can be fitted with the Field Artillery Computer Equipment. Laden weight is 10,620kg.
Other Projects/Variants: There was a project to fit Swingfire ATGW to a Saracen but this progressed only as far as the mock up stage. An FV 610 vehicle was used as a test vehicle for the GS No 9 Mk 1 Radar called Robert, this did not,

however, enter service. Some Saracens were built without roofs for operation in the Middle East.
Employment
In service with Abu Dhabi, Brunei, Great Britain, Hong Kong (Police), Indonesia, Jordan, Kuwait (open topped versions), Libya, Nigeria, South Africa, Sudan, Thailand, Uganda, Qatar.

Short SB. 301
Armoured Personnel Carrier

Great Britain

Armament: None
Crew: 2 + 6
Length: 4.292m
Width: 1.764m
Height: 2.159m
G/Clearance: .21m
Weight: 3543kg (loaded)
Track: 1.358m
Engine: 6 cylinder Rover water-cooled petrol engine developing 91 bhp at 4500rpm
Speed: 96km/hr
Range: 368km
Fuel: 50 litres (standard)
100 litres (long range)
Armour: 6.35mm

Development
The Short SB.301 armoured personnel carrier has been designed by Short Brothers and Harland of Belfast, Northern Ireland, to meet a requirement for a simple and reliable APC for use in Internal Security operations, and to operate with the Shorland armoured patrol car. The first

prototype was completed in 1973 with production vehicles following in 1974.
The SB.301 is essentially a modified long wheel base Land Rover chassis with a new armoured body. The six passengers are carried in the rear of the hull and a total of eight firing ports are provided. The hull is of all welded construction whilst the floor is of glass reinforced plastic. The basic vehicle is unarmed although four smoke/tear gas dischargers can be mounted each side of the roof if required. Optional equipment includes various radio installations and run-flat tyres.
Variants
There are no variants of the Short SB.301.
Employment
In service with eight countries including Great Britain (RUC) and The Netherlands (airport police).

Below: *The Short SB.301 Armoured Patrol Carrier*

Sankey Internal Security Vehicles   Great Britain

	AT-104	AT-105
Crew:	2 + 9	2 + 8
Length:	5.486m	5.17m
Width:	2.438m	2.489m
Height:	2.489m	2.59m
	(cupola)	(cupola)
G/Clearance:	.457m (hull)	.36m (hull)
Weight Loaded:	8900kg	9144kg
Weight Empty:	8000kg	8230kg
Road Speed:	80km/hr	88.5km/hr
Range:	640km	640km
Fuel:	160 litres	160 litres
Fording:	.7m	1.12m
Engine:	6 cyl. Bedford petrol (134bhp) or 6 cyl. diesel (98bhp)	6 cyl. Bedford diesel (146bhp) or Rolls-Royce 8 cyl. petrol (164bhp)

Development

In 1971, GKN Sankey of Wellington, Shropshire, designed a 4 x 2 IS vehicle called the AT-100, this was not placed in production and was followed by the AT-104 (4 x 4) in 1972 and then by the AT-105 (4 x 4) in 1974. Both of these vehicles use standard Bedford automotive components with a new hull of all welded steel construction, this varies in thickness from 6mm to 12.5mm, firing ports are provided in the hull sides and rear. A wide range of equipment can be fitted including an air-conditioning system, heater, searchlight, grenade launchers, winch, barricade removers and so on. A variety of armament installations are available including a turret mounted 7.62mm machine gun.

Variants:

The basic vehicles can also be adopted for use as ambulances, cargo carriers and command vehicles.

Employment

AT-104s are used by the Dutch State Police and the Royal Brunei Malaya Regiment. The AT-105 has been ordered by at least one country.

Right: *The Sankey AT-104 Internal Security Vehicle*

Below: *The Sankey AT-105 Internal Security Vehicle*

Humber 1 Ton Armoured Truck (FV1611)

Great Britain

Crew: 2 + 6/8
Length: 4.93m
Width: 2.05m
Height: 2.12m
Weight: 5790kg (loaded)
4770kg (empty)
Engine: Rolls-Royce B60 6 cylinder petrol engine developing 120hp at 3750rpm
Speed: 64km/ph (road)
Range: 400km
Fuel: 145 litres
Wheelbase: 2.74m
Track: 1.72m

Development/Variants

The FV 1611 was developed from the earlier FV 1609A armoured truck which in turn was based on the chassis of the Humber FV 1601A one-ton cargo truck. The chassis was made by Humber and the body by J. Sankey Limited or the Royal Ordnance Factories. The basic vehicles are:

FV 1611: Used to transport personnel and stores, also used to tow the Green Archer Mortar Locating Radar system.

FV 1612: This is a radio vehicle and has a crew of three, driver, commander and radio operator.

FV 1613: Ambulance version. Crew of two, driver and medical orderly. Can carry three stretcher or eight sitting, or one stretcher and four sitting patients.

FV 1620: Hornet/Malkara vehicle is no longer in service having been replaced by the Ferret Mk 5.

Employment

Used by the British Army and Portugal. The vehicles are widely used in Northern Ireland. In 1972/1973 some 500 of these vehicles were fitted with additional armour. Some have also been provided with searchlights and tear/smoke grenade launchers.

The Humber 1 Ton Armoured 4 × 4 Truck in Northern Ireland

Abbot – Self-Propelled Gun   Great Britain
Falcon – Self-Propelled Anti-Aircraft System

	Abbot	V/E Abbot	Falcon
Crew:	4	4	3
Length Overall:	5.84m	5.714m	5.333m
Length Hull:	5.709m	5.333m	5.333m
Width:	2.641m	2.641m	2.641m
Height:	2.489m	2.489m	2.514m
G/Clearance:	.406m	.406m	.406m
Weigth Loaded:	16,556kg	15,900kg	15,850kg
Weight Empty:	14,878kg	14,200kg	14,300kg
G/Pressure:	.89kg.cm^2	.81kg.cm^2	.81kg.cm^2
Speed Road:	48km/ph	48km/ph	48km/ph
Range Road:	390km	390km	390km
Fuel:	386 litres	386 litres	386 litres
Fording:	1.219m	1.117m	1.117m
V/Obstacle:	.609m	.609m	.609m
Trench:	2.057m	2.057m	2.057m
Gradient:	60%	60%	60%
Main Armament Calibre:	105mm	105mm	—
Anti-Aircraft Calibre:	7.62mm	—	30mm
Ammunition Main:	40	36	—
Ammunition A/A:	1200	—	620
Armour:	6mm–12mm	6mm–12mm	6mm–12mm

Development
Development of the Abbot commenced in 1958, the design parents being Vickers Limited. The first of 12 prototypes was completed in 1961. After trials a production order was awarded to Vickers Limited. The Abbot was in production at Vickers Elswick Works from 1964 until 1967. The Abbot uses many components of the FV 432 series of armoured personnel carriers.

Variants
Abbot (FV 433): The Abbot is armed with a 105mm gun in a turret with a traverse of 360°, the gun has an elevation of +70° and a depression of −5°. Sustained rate of fire is 12 rounds a minute. The gun has a maximum range of 17,000m and six different types of shell are available. A 7.62mm anti-aircraft machine gun is mounted for the use of the commander and there are three smoke dischargers

mounted either side of the turret. The Abbot is fitted with an NBC system and infra-red driving lights. A flotation screen is carried around the top of the hull, when erected this enables the vehicle to cross rivers. It is propelled in the water by its tracks at about 5km/ph. The Abbot is powered by a Rolls-Royce K60 Mk 4G, 6 cylinder, in line, multi-fuel engine developing 240bhp at 2750rpm.

Value Engineered Abbot: The first prototype was completed in 1971 and it has been built at Vickers Elswick Works for the Indian Army. The Value Engineered Abbot is basically a standard Abbot with non-essential equipment removed, more economical components have been used. It lacks such items as the NBC system and the floatation screen as a number of Armies have no requirement for these. Any of these components could be added at a later date. It must be emphasised that there has been no degradation of standards or materials. The Value Engineered Abbot is powered by a Rolls-Royce K60 Mk 60G/1, 6 cylinder, in line diesel engine developing 213bhp at 3750rpm.

Falcon: The Falcon anti-aircraft system is a Value Engineered Abbot chassis fitted with a turret designed by the British Manufacture and Research Company. The turret mounts two Hispano Suiza 831L guns, these have an elevation of +85° and a depression of −10°, traverse and elevation is powered. The 30mm guns fire a wide range of ammunition and have a maximum range in the anti-aircraft role of 3000m. They are also highly effective in the ground role, especially against lightly armoured vehicles such as APCs. Their combined rate of fire is 1300 rounds per minute. The vehicle is powered by a Rolls-Royce Mk 60G/2, 6 cylinder, in line, water-cooled diesel engine developing 213bhp at 3750rpm. Trials have been completed and the vehicle is ready for production. Vickers now specify the GM V6-53 Diesel developing 216bhp at 2800rpm for both the V/E Abbot and the Falcon, and this would be fitted to production vehicles.

Employment

Abbot is used by the British Royal Artillery. Value Engineered Abbot is used by the Indian Army.

Below left:
The Falcon Anti-Aircraft System uses the same chassis as the Value Engineered Abbot

Below:
An Abbot Self-Propelled Gun

FV 180 Combat Engineered Tractor   Great Britain

Crew: 2
Length: 7.544m (overall)
5.334m (hull)
Width: 2.896m (bucket)
Height: 2.667m (overall)
G /Clearance: 0.457m
Weight: 17,100kg
G /Pressure: 0.435kg /cm²
Engine: Rolls-Royce C6TFR 6 cylinder in-line diesel developing 320hp
Speed: 56km /hr (road)
8km /hr (water)
Fuel: 430 litres
Fording: 1.829m
V /Obstacle: 0.61m
Trench: 2.06m
Gradient: 60%

Development /Variants
The FV 180 Combat Engineer Tractor (CET) has been developed by the Military Vehicles and Engineering Establishment to meet the requirements of the Royal Engineers. The first test rigs were completed in 1968 with prototypes following in 1973 /74. It is now in production at the Royal Ordnance Factory at Leeds and should enter service with the British Army in 1977. It will take over some of the roles now being carried out by the Centurion AVRE. Its crew of two consists of the driver and operator and is normally driven with the bucket to the rear. The latter is hydraulically operated and can be used for a variety of roles. These include the preparing of river crossings, preparation of gun and tank pits as well as clearing battlefield obstacles. A crane can be installed in the bucket if required. A hydraulic winch with 107m of rope is provided and this can be led out either the front or rear of the hull. If the CET becomes stuck in a river or similar obstacle, then it can launch its earth anchor. This is rocket propelled and is attached to 91m of rope. When emplaced it enables the CET to winch itself out. A NBC system is provided as is passive rather than infra-red driving equipment. No armament is fitted although smoked dischargers are mounted. The CET can also tow a trailer fitted with the Giant Viper Mine Clearance system. It can ford to a depth of 1.829m without preparation. Flotation equipment designed by FPT Industries of Portsmouth can be quickly installed and it then propels itself in the water by two waterjets, one in each side of the hull.

Employment
In production for the British Army.

The FV 180 Combat Engineered Tractor launching its earth anchor

FUG Reconnaissance Vehicles   Hungary

	FUG-70	FUG-63
Crew:	3 + 6	5
Length:	5.79m	5.79m
Width:	2.362m	2.362m
Height:	2.525m (turret)	2.25m
G/Clearance:	.305m	.305m
Weight laden:	7000kg	6100kg
Speed road:	100km/hr	87km/hr
Speed water:	10km/hr	9km/hr
Range:	500km	500km
Fording:	Amphibious	Amphibious
V/Obstacle:	.4m	.4m
Gradient:	60%	60%
Engine:	6 cylinder diesel	4 cylinder diesel
Armour:	10mm	10mm

Development/Variants
The FUG-70 (Felderito Uszo Gepkocsi) was first seen in 1970 and was preceded by a development model known as the FUG-66. The FUG-70 is fully amphibious being propelled in the water by two water-jets. It is armed with a turret mounted 14.5mm KPVT and a 7.62mm PKT co-axial machine gun, these have an elevation of +30° and a depression of −5°. Total ammunition capacity is 500 rounds of 14.5mm and 2000 rounds of 7.62mm ammunition. The FUG-70 does not have any belly wheels. Equipment provided includes a NBC system, infra-red night vision equipment and a central tyre pressure regulation system. There is also a command version of the FUG-70, this does not have a turret.

FUG-63. This is called the OT-65 by Czechoslovakia. It is armed with a 7.62mm SGMB machine gun on a pintle mount, this has a traverse of 90° and a total of 1250 rounds of ammunition are carried. Like the Russian BRDM-2, the FUG-63 is provided with belly wheels to improve cross country mobility. There are three versions—(1) Ambulance (2) Radio-logical-Chemical reconnaissance vehicle (3) The Czechs use a model with the same turret as fitted to the OT-62B APC.

Employment
FUG-70—East Germany and Hungary.
FUG-63—Czechoslovakia, Hungary, Poland and Romania.

Below: *The FUG-63 4 × 4 reconnaissance vehicle*

RBY Mk. 1 Armoured Reconnaissance Vehicle   Israel

Armament: See text below
Crew: 2 + 6
Length: 5.023m
Width: 2.03m
Height: 1.66m (w /o armament)
G /Clearance: .48m (hull)
.35m (transfer case)
Weight: 3600kg (empty)
Engine: Dodge Model 225.2, 6 cylinder water cooled petrol engine developing 120hp
Speed: 100km /hr (road)
Range: 550km (road)
400km (cross country)
Fuel: 140 litres
Fording: .4m
Gradient: 60%
Armour: 10mm (maximum)

Development
The RBY Mk 1 Armoured Reconnaissance Vehicle has been designed by Ramta Structures and Systems, which is itself a Division of Israel Aircraft Industries. The vehicle was first shown in 1975 and it has been reported that it is now in production for the Israeli Army and for export. The driver and commander are seated at the front of the vehicle whilst the six passengers are seated to the rear, three down each side of the hull. There is no overhead protection for the crew and passengers' compartment in the RBY Mk 1. It does not have a NBC system and has no amphibious capabilities. The vehicle can be carried internally by the Sikorsky CH-53 Helicopters which is used by the Israeli Air Force.

Variants
The basic vehicle is normally armed with up to four 7.62mm or 12.7mm machine guns on individual mounts around the top of the hull. Other variants include an anti-tank model with a single 106mm M40 Recoilless Rifle which is made in Israel by Israel Military Industries and an anti-aircraft vehicle with two 20mm rapid fire cannon, the latter have been developed from a French 20mm gun by Ramta Structures. If required a winch with a capacity of 2722kg can be mounted at the front of the hull.

Employment
Reported to be in service with the Israeli Army.

Below: *RBY. Mk. 1 Armed with a 106mm Recoilless Rifle*

Israel

Israel has been modifying and adapting armoured fighting vehicles to its own requirements for many years. Below is a resumé of some of these modifications.
Ben-Gurion: This is the Centurion MBT fitted with the French 105mm gun. It would seem, however, that there are few of these, if any, in service, as most Israeli Centurions are armed with the British 105mm gun.
Super-Sherman: This is a Sherman fitted with a French 75mm gun similar to that used in the AMX-13 light tank. In addition the turret rear has been modified and two smoke dischargers fitted either side of the turret. Israel has captured

a number of Shermans from the Egyptian Army fitted with the complete turret of the AMX-13 light tank. These have most probably been used as chassis for self-propelled guns.

Isherman: This is a Sherman fitted with a French 105mm gun and a new 500hp Pratt and Whitney R-1340-AN-1 petrol engine. This new engine gives the vehicle a higher speed. The steering and transmission have been replaced and a new exhaust installed. Some Ishermans have been fitted with wider tracks. Smoke dischargers are fitted to either side of the turret.

Sherman: Shermans used for the Super-Sherman and Isherman conversions include the M-4A1, M-4A2 and M-4A3. Some of these have vertical volute spring suspensions and some horizontal volute spring suspension. It would appear that all Sherman gun tanks will eventually be converted to either self-propelled artillery or self-propelled mortar roles.

Sherman-Flail: Israel used Sherman flail tanks for mine-clearing operations during the six-day war of 1967.

AMX-13: Israel has sold all of her AMX-13s as these were found unsuitable for desert operations. The AMX 105mm self-propelled guns will probably be phased out in the near future as the standard Israeli SPG is now a 155mm weapon.

Centurion: First shown in 1973 was the new Israeli Centurion. The Israelis have fitted a new Continental 750hp diesel, GE hydraulic gearbox, 105mm gun, more fuel capacity, in all over 2000 modifications have been made. This gives the vehicle twice the range and increases its maximum speed to 43km/ph, as well as making the vehicle more reliable.

M-48: Israel has received M-48A1, M-48A2 and M-48A2Cs from the United States and Germany. The following modifications have been carried out which bring the vehicle up to M-60 standards: 105mm gun fitted, Continental diesel engine, wider tracks and an XENON searchlight. Some M-48s have a smaller commander's cupola and an open 12.7mm machine gun.

T-54 and T-55: Israel has rebuilt many captured Soviet T-54 and T-55 tanks. These are called TI-67 and are not liked by the Israelis. The modifications have included the fitting of an American diesel engine, the 100mm gun has been replaced by a 105mm British gun, a 12.7mm anti-aircraft machine gun has replaced the Soviet one, a fire control system has been installed as has a new electrical system and air-conditioning.

Sabra: Early in 1970 it was reported that Israel had a prototype of a new MBT under test, this being designed and built in Israel.

Early reports indicated that it had a 120mm gun but later reports state that it has a 105mm gun, a laser rangefinder and an American Continental diesel engine. Recently some reports have indicated that the Sabra is in fact the Centurion rebuilt in Israel.

155mm Self-Propelled Howitzer: This is simply an M-7 Priest or Sherman chassis fitted with the French 155mm M-1950 weapon. It was first seen in 1964. A more recent 155mm weapon is the L-33 (see separate entry).

160mm Self-Propelled Mortar Carrier: This is an M-7 or M-4 Sherman chassis on which has been mounted a 160mm Soltam mortar. When in action the sides and front of the vehicle can be folded horizontal thus providing space for the crew of 4—7 men to load the weapon. The mortar has a maximum range of 9600m and is breech loaded. A high rate of fire can be achieved. A 12.7mm anti-aircraft machine gun is fitted.

Half-Tracks: The Israeli Army has adapted many M-2 and M-3 half-tracks for various roles including ambulances, command vehicles, ammunition vehicles, load carriers and engineer vehicles. Other versions include:

Missile: This had four SS-11 ATGW mounted in the ready-to-fire position, it is doubtful if these are still in service.

Anti-Aircraft: This is armed with 2 x 20mm cannon.

Mortar: This is armed with a Soltam 120mm mortar which has a range of 400m—6500m. Over 30 rounds of ammunition are carried. The mortar can also be moved from the vehicle for firing.

Anti-Tank: Armed with a 106mm recoilless rifle.

Anti-Tank: Armed with a 90mm Mecar gun.

Soviet and Egyptian APCs: The Israeli Army have adapted BTR-40, BTR-50, BTR-152 and the Egyptian Walid APCs to their own requirements. The wheeled vehicles are used in the internal security role.

L–33 Self-Propelled Gun/Howitzer   Israel

Armament: 1 × 155mm howitzer
1 × 7.62mm anti-aircraft machine gun
Crew: 8
Length: 8.47m (with armament)
6.47m (hull)
Width: 3.45m
Height: 3.45m
G/Clearance: .43m
Weight: 41,500kg
G/Pressure: .84kg/cm²
Engine: Cummins VT 8-460-B1, diesel
developing 460hp at 2600rpm
Speed: 36km/hr
Range: 260km
Fuel: 640 litres
Fording: .9m
V/Obstacle: .91m
Trench: 2.3m
Gradient: 60%
Armour: 64mm (max)

Development/Variants

The L-33 has been in service with the
Israeli Army since 1972 and was used for
the first time operationally in the 1973
Middle East conflict. It consists of a Super
Sherman chassis (with horizontal volute
suspension) on which has been mounted
a Soltam/Tampella 155mm howitzer with
armour protection. This weapon has an
elevation of +52° and a depression of
−3°, total traverse being 30° left and 30°
right. It fires a projectile weighing 43.4kg
with a m/v of 725 m/s to a maximum
range of 21,500m. A total of 60 rounds
of ammunition are carried, of these 16

are ready for immediate use. The ammunition consists of the projectile, cartridge and
the charge. An automatic compressed air
rammer is mounted on the cradle and this
can be used at all angles of elevation. A
7.62mm machine gun with a traverse of
360° is mounted on the right side of the
roof, this can be used against both ground
and air targets.

Employment
In service with the Israeli Army.

This was announced in 1975. It consists
of a rebuilt Centurion tank chassis on
which has been mounted a new turret
mounting a 155mm Soltam howitzer. This
turret can be traversed through 360° and
the main armament can be elevated from
−3° to +65°. A total of 60 rounds of
ammunition are carried, of these 34 are
in the turret and 26 in the hull. An
automatic rammer is provided. According
to Soltam, this turret could also be
mounted on other MBT chassis such as
the M47 or M48.

Employment
Trials. Not yet in service.

*Below: The L-33 Self-Propelled
Gun/Howitzer*

*Top right: 120mm mortar mounted in
Half-Track of the Israeli Army*

*Bottom right: 155mm Centurion Self-
Propelled Howitzer*

Fiat/Oto Melara 6616M

Italy

Armament: 1 x 20mm Rh.202 cannon with an elevation of + 35° and a depression of − 5°
1 x 7.62mm machine gun co-axial with main armament
2 x 3 smoke dischargers either side of turret
1 x smoke grenade launcher in turret roof
400 rounds of 20mm ammunition
1000 rounds of 7.62mm ammunition
44 smoke grenades
Crew: 3
Length: 5.235m
Width: 2.5m
Height: 1.98m (top of turret)
1.48m (top of hull)
G/Clearance: .37m
Weight: 7400kg (loaded)
6900kg (empty)
Engine: Six cylinder in-line, direct injection turbocharged diesel developing 147bhp at 3200rpm
Speed: 95km/hr (road)
4.5km/hr (water)
Range: 750km
Fuel: 120 litres
Fording: Amphibious
V/Obstacle: .45m
Gradient: 60%
Armour: 6–8mm

Development

The 6616M is a joint development by Fiat of Turin and Oto Melara of La Spezia. The first prototype was completed in 1972 and the first production order is for a total of 50 vehicles. Of these 30 are for the police and the remaining 20 for the army. It has a hull of all welded steel construction with the fighting compartment at the front of the hull and the engine, transmission and fuel at the rear. The commander and the gunner are both seated in the turret which has full powered traverse through 360°. If required a 40mm automatic grenade launcher or a TOW/Milan anti-tank missile system can be mounted on the turret roof. The 6616M is fully amphibious being propelled in the water by its wheels. Equipment fitted as standard includes a NBC system, electric bilge pumps, winch with a capacity of 3000kg, run-flat tyres, infra-red driving lights, an air-conditioning system and a fire extinguishing system.

Variants: There are no variants of the 6616M armoured car although it does use a number of automotive components of the Type 6614 armoured personnel carrier. According to the manufacturers of the 6616M, the vehicle could be fitted with other types of armament installations and other types of turret, including those fitted to the French Panhard AML armoured car.

Employment
In service with the Italian Army and Police.

Below: *The Fiat/Oto Melara Type 6616M armoured car*

88

Top: *Alvis Saladin Armoured Car.*   Above: *GKN Sankey AT-105 IS Vehicle.*

Top: *FV432 Armoured Personnel Carrier.*   Above: *M109A1's of the Spanish Army.*

Top: *Panhard M3 APC with 20mm cannon.*   Above: *Berliet VXB with 7.62mm MG.*

Above: *Saviem 6x6 VAB.*

Top right: *Jagdpanzer Rakete.*

Bottom right: *Centurion Bridgelayer.*

Top: *FMC XR-311 Reconnaissance Vehicle.*

Above: *M60 AVLB of Spanish Army.*

Top right: *Alvis Striker.*

Bottom right: *Ferret Mk2/6 with Vigilant ATGW.*

Top: *Leopard A1 (right) and A4 (left) MBT's.*

Above: *AMX 30 MBT of Spanish Army.*

Fiat 6614 CM Armoured Personnel Carrier   Italy

Armament: 1 × 12.7mm machine gun
Crew: 2 + 8 /9
Length: 5.56m (5.86m)
Width: 2.37m (2.5m)
Height: 1.68m (1.78m)
(top of hull)
G /Clearance: .35m (.37m)
Weight Loaded: 7000kg (7200kg)
Weight Empty: 5850kg (6150kg)
Engine: Fiat Model 8062 6 cylinder
water cooled diesel developing 128hp at
3200rpm
(6 cylinder diesel developing 147hp at
3200rpm)
Speed: 96km /hr (96km /hr)
3.5km /hr (water)
Range: 700km (700km)
Fuel: 120 litres
V /Obstacle: .45m
Gradient: 60%
Armour: 6–8mm
Note. *Data in brackets relate to the Fiat
6614M APC.*

Development
The Fiat 6614 CM armoured personnel
carrier is a development of the earlier Fiat
6614 BM, the latter did not enter production however. The 6614 shares many
automotive components with the Fiat
6616 4 × 4 armoured car which is now
in production for the Italian Army and
Police. The most recent model of the 6614
is the 6614M which has a more powerful
diesel engine.

It has a hull of all welded steel construction
which gives the crew protection from small
arms fire. There is a single door in each
side of the hull and a large ramp in the hull
rear, firing ports are provided in the hull
sides and rear. The vehicle is fully amphibious being propelled in the water by its
wheels. Run-flat tyres are fitted and the
steering is power assisted. An NBC system
can be installed as can night vision equipment.

Variants
The 6614 CM can be used as an APC,
cargo carrier, ambulance or internal
security vehicle. It is normally armed with
a single 12.7mm machine gun on a ring
mount. Other armament installations are
possible including a 20mm cannon or
various ATGWs.

Employment
Not yet in production.

Below: *The Fiat 6614 4 × 4 amphibious
armoured personnel carrier*

Type 74 Main Battle Tank

Japan

Armament: 1 x 105mm gun (L-7A1)
1 x 7.62mm co-axial machine gun
1 x 12.7mm anti-aircraft machine gun (M-2)
2 x 3 smoke dischargers either side of turret
Crew: 4
Length: 9.088m (gun forward)
6.85m (hull)
Width: 3.18m
Height: 2.25m (normal)
G/Clearance: .40m (normal)
(min .2m max .6m)
Weight: 38,000kg (loaded)
Engine: Mitsubishi 10ZF Type 21 WT, 10 cylinder diesel, air-cooled, developing 750hp at 2200rpm
Speed: 53km/ph (road)
Range: 500km
Fuel: 700 litres
Fording: 1.00m
3m (with schnorkel)
V/Obstacle: 1.00m
Trench: 2.70m
Gradient: 60%
G/Pressure: .85kg.cm^2

Development/Variants

In 1962 Japan started to design a new tank for the 1970s. The first prototypes were built in 1968/1969, and these underwent trials from the end of 1969. The original prototypes were called STB-1s. These had a remote controlled machine gun towards the rear of the turret. Later models, the STB-3 had a 105mm L7A3

gun, the anti-aircraft gun has a simple open type mount between the commander's and loader's hatch, also the turret rear has been altered and a stowage box added. The first models had a semi-automatic loading system for the 105mm gun.

The Type 74 has adjustable hydro-pneumatic suspension. This allows the height of the tank to be adjusted according to the tactical situation. A schnorkel can be fitted for deep wading. Infra-red driving lights are fitted and an infra-red/white light searchlight is mounted to the left of the main gun. A Japanese-built laser range-finder and gun stabilisation system is installed as is an NBC system.

The Type 74 is built by Mitsubishi Heavy Industries, the 105mm gun is now built in Japan by the Japan Steel Works.

Variants

A dozer blade has been fitted for trial purposes. A 155mm SPG has been developed to the prototype stage. This weighs 24,000kg and is powered by a diesel which develops 420hp and gives it a top speed of 50km/hr. The gun has a traverse of 360°, elevation being from + 65° to − 5°.

Employment

In production for the Japanese Self-Defence Force.

Type 74 Main Battle Tank

Type 61 Main Battle Tank   Japan

Armament: 1 x 90mm Type 61 gun
1 x 7.62mm M-1919A4 co-axial machine gun
1 x 12.7mm M-2 anti-aircraft machine gun
Crew: 4
Length: 8.19m (gun forward)
6.30m (hull)
Width: 2.95m
Height: 3.16m (with A/A machine gun)
2.49m (turret roof)
G/Clearance: .40m
Weight: 35,000kg (loaded)
Engine: Mitsubishi Type 12 HM 21 WT, V-12, turbo-charged air-cooled diesel developing 600hp at 2100rpm
Speed: 45km/ph (road)
Range: 200km (road)
Fording: .99m
V/Obstacle: .685m
Trench: 2.489m
Gradient: 60%
Armour: 64mm
G/Pressure: .95kg.cm²

Development
Design work on the Type 61 started in 1954 and it was the first tank to be built in Japan since the end of World War II. The first prototypes were completed in March 1957 and these were called the ST-A1 and ST-A2. The ST-A1 had seven road wheels and four return rollers and the ST-A2 had six road wheels and three return rollers, both tanks were armed with a 90mm gun. After extensive trials a further series of vehicles were built, these being called the ST-A3 and ST-A4. These were completed in 1958/1959. After trials, production commenced in 1962 by Mitsubishi Nippon Heavy Industries and the tank was named 'Type 61'. The hundredth Type 61 was completed in November 1966.

The Type 61 can be fitted with infra-red driving and fighting equipment. It does not have an NBC system and cannot be fitted with a schnorkel.

Variants
Type 67 Armoured Vehicle Launched Bridge: This is similar to the American AVLB on the M-48/M-60 chassis. Weight 35,000kg, length 7.27m, width 3.50m, height 3.50m, crew three, armament 1 x 7.62mm machine gun.

Type 70 Armoured Recovery Vehicle: This has a boom and a dozer blade. Weight 35,000kg, length 8.40m, width 2.95m, height 3.10m, armament 1 x 81mm mortar, 1 x 7.62mm machine gun, 1 x 12.7mm machine gun, crew four.

Type 67 Armoured Engineering Vehicle: Weight 35,000kg, length 7.46m, width 3.20m, height 2.23m, armament 1 x 7.62mm and 1 x 12.7mm machine guns, crew four.

Employment
Used only by the Japanese Self-Defence Force (Army). Production complete.

Type 61 Main Battle Tank, this particular model is fitted with infra-red driving lights

Type 73 Mechanised Infantry Combat Vehicle   Japan

Armament: 1 × 12.7mm machine gun on roof of vehicle
1 × 7.62mm machine gun in bow of vehicle
Crew: 2 + 10
Length: 5.80m
Width: 2.80m
Height: 1.70m (w/o armament)
Weight: 14,000kg (loaded)
Engine: Mitsubishi V4, 2 cycle, air-cooled diesel, supercharged developing 300hp at 2200rpm.
Speed: 60km/ph (road)
Fording: Amphibious
Trench: 2.1m
Gradient: 60%
Armour: Aluminium

Development/Variants
This has been designed and manufactured by Mitsubishi Heavy Industries to replace the Type SU 60 armoured personnel carriers at present used by the Japanese Self-Defence Force. The Type 73 is fully amphibious being propelled in the water by its tracks, a small trim board is erected before the vehicle enters the water. Other features of the vehicle include a hull of aluminium armour, NBC system infra-red driving and fighting lights. Some models have been seen with small firing ports in either side of the hull.
There are two models of the Type 73. The

Model 1 (SUB 1) is armed with a bow-mounted machine gun and a simple 12.7mm machine gun mount on the roof. At the rear of the vehicle are six smoke dischargers (three each side). The Model 11 has a turret-mounted 12.7mm machine gun with three smoke dischargers mounted either side of the turret. It also has the bow-mounted machine gun. Other versions of the Type 73 are probably under development.
Employment
In production for the Japanese Self-Defence Force.

Above: *Type 73 MICV Model 1*

Type SU 60 Armoured Personnel Carrier Japan

Armament: 1 × 12.7mm M-2 machine gun, on roof
1 × 7.62mm M-1919A4 machine gun, bow mounted.
Crew: 2 + 8
Length: 4.85m
Width: 2.40m
Height: 2.31m (including machine gun) 1.70m (w/o machine gun)
G/Clearance: .40m
Weight: 11,800kg (loaded) 10,600kg (empty)
Engine: Mitsubishi 8 HA-21 WT, V-8, air-cooled turbo-charged diesel developing 220hp at 2400rpm
Speed: 45km/ph
Range: 230km
Fording: .76m
V/Obstacle: .60m
Trench: 1.82m
Gradient: 60%
G/Pressure: .57kg.cm²

Development
Development of the SU armoured personnel carrier started in 1956 and prototypes were built by two companies. Komatsu built the SU-1 and Mitsubishi built the SU-2. These prototypes were completed in 1957. The trials showed that the Mitsubishi vehicle was the better and after some re-design the vehicle was placed in production at the Maruko plant of

Mitsubishi Heavy Industries. The first production vehicle was completed in 1960 and production continued until 1970 by which time over 400 had been built. The SU 60 does not have any amphibious capability, nor does it have an NBC system or any infra-red driving lights.

Variants
81mm Mortar Carrier (SV): Crew five, armed with an 81mm mortar in the rear of the vehicle. It retains its 12.7mm and 7.62mm machine guns. A baseplate and stand are carried on the front of the vehicle enabling the mortar to be dismounted and fired away from the vehicle.
107mm Mortar (4.2in) Carrier (SX): Crew five and has a loaded weight of 12,900kg. The mortar is mounted in the rear of the vehicle and this model can easily be recognised as the rear of the hull is cut at an angle. The 12.7mm machine gun is retained. A baseplate and stand is carried on the front of the vehicle enabling the mortar to be fired away from the vehicle.
105mm Howitzer (SY): Did not progress beyond the prototype stage.

Employment
Used only by the Japanese Self-Defence Force (Army).

Above: *Type SU 60 APC*

Type 60 Self-Propelled 106mm Recoilless Rifle   Japan

Armament: 2 x 106mm recoilless rifles
with 10 rounds of ammunition
1 x 12.7mm spotting machine gun
Crew: 3
Length: 4.30m
Width: 2.23m
Height: 1.38m
G /Clearance: .35m
Weight: 8020kg (loaded)
7600kg (empty)
G /Pressure: .63kg.cm²
Engine: Komatsu T 120, 6 cylinder, air-cooled diesel developing 120hp at 2400rpm
Speed: 48km /ph (road)
Range: 130km (road)
Fuel: 77 litres
Fording: .80m
V /Obstacle: .53m
Trench: 1.78m
Gradient: 67%
Armour: 15mm–30mm

Development /Variants
Design of this vehicle started in 1954 and it was the first postwar Japanese armoured fighting vehicle. Prototypes were built by Komatsu (SS-1) and Mitsubishi (SS-2); these were completed at the end of 1955. The SS-1 had its engine at the front with its driving sprocket at the rear, the SS-2 having its engine at the rear and its driving sprocket at the front. They both had different suspensions. They were both armed with 2 x 105mm recoilless rifles. The vehicles were subjected to extensive trials and the SS-2 was found to be the better of the two vehicles. These were followed by the SS-3 in 1956 and the SS-4 in 1959. In 1960 a production order was placed for the Type 60. Manufacturers involved were Komatsu, Japan Steel Works and the Howa Machinery Company. Production has been completed.

When in the lowered position the rifles have an elevation of + 10° and a depression of − 5°, traverse being 10° left and 10° right. When raised with their mount they have an elevation of + 25° and a depression of − 15°, traverse being 30° left and 30° right. The 106mm rifles can fire HE and anti-tank rounds, maximum range being 1100m. Rate of fire, 6 rounds per minute. The rifles weigh 114kg, overall length being 3.408m, barrel length 3.332m.

The Type SU 60 does not have any infra-red driving lights nor does it have an NBC system.

Employment
Used only by the Japanese Self-Defence Force (Army).

Type 60 Self-Propelled 106mm Recoilless Rifle

YP–408 Armoured Personnel Carrier   Netherlands

Armament: 1 × 12.7mm machine gun, elevation + 70°, depression −8°
2 × 3 barrelled smoke dischargers
Crew: 2 + 10
Length: 6.23m
Width: 2.40m
Height: 2.37m (including machine gun) 1.80m (hull top)
G /Clearance: .457m
Weight: 12,000kg (loaded) 9500kg (empty)
Track: 2.054m (front)
Engine: DAF DS 575, 6 cylinder, in-line, water-cooled, turbo-charged diesel developing 165hp at 2400rpm
Speed: 80km /ph (road)
Range: 500km (road) 400km (cross country)
Fuel: 200 litres
Fording: 1.20m
V /Obstacle: .70m
Trench: 1.20m
Gradient: 60%
Armour: 16mm (maximum)

Development
The YP-408 was designed by Van Doorne's Automobielfabriek (DAF) NV of Eindhoven. The first mock-up was completed in 1957 and the first prototype was completed in 1958. The prototypes were followed by a pre-production batch. The first production vehicle was completed in 1964 and the last in 1968, about 750 of all versions were built. The vehicle uses many components of the YA-328 artillery tractor.
The vehicle is an 8 × 6, the front two and rear four being powered, steering is hydraulically assisted and is on the front four wheels. The vehicle is not amphibious, capable only of fording. It does not have an NBC system although a heater is fitted, infra-red driving and fighting lights can be fitted. There are a total of 6 roof hatches; at the rear are two doors, these being provided with a firing port each.
The basic vehicle is designated PWI-S, which means Panser Wagen Infanterie—Standard.

Variants
PWI-S (PC): This is a platoon commander's vehicle and has a crew of nine and additional radios.
PWCO: This is a company and battalion commander's vehicle and has a crew of six men. It has map tables and additional batteries and a tent can be erected at the rear if required.
PW-GWT: This is an ambulance and does not have any armament. It has a crew of three and can carry two stretcher patients and four sitting patients.
PW-V: This is a freight carrier and can carry 1500kg of freight. It has a crew of two and does not have a radio. If required it can also be used as an ambulance.
PW-MT: This is a mortar-towing vehicle and tows the French Brandt 120mm mortar. A total of 50 rounds of ammunition are carried; it has a crew of seven. The rear doors are slightly different on this model.

Employment
Used only by the Netherlands Army.

The YP-408 PW-MT towing 120mm mortar

T-64/T-72 Main Battle Tank　　　Soviet Union

Armament: 1 x 125mm gun
1 x 7.62mm machine gun co-axial with main armament
1 x 12.7mm anti-aircraft machine gun
Crew: 3
Length: 10.1m (gun forwards)
7.4m (hull)
Width: 3.3m
Height: 2.46m (w/o A/A MG)
Weight: 40,000kg (loaded)
Engine: Water-cooled diesel developing between 900 and 1000hp
Speed: 60km/hr
Range: 500km
Fording: 1.4m
5m (with schnorkel)
V/Obstacle: .8m
Trench: 2.8m
Gradient: 60%
Note: *The above data is provisional*

Development
The T-64 (or T-72 as it is also known) entered service with the Russian Army in 1973/74 and was preceded by an experimental tank known as the M-1970. The latter is reported to have had the same gun as the T-62 but fitted with a fully-automatic loading system, and hence a crew of three men.
The T-64 has a new chassis which is a departure from that used on the T-34/T-44/T-54/T-62 series. This has a total of six road wheels with the drive sprocket at the rear and the idler at the front. The tank is armed with a 125mm (some sources state 122mm) smoothbore gun. This is fed from an automatic loader which holds a total of 28 ready use rounds. This allows the crew to be reduced to three men—commander, gunner and driver. The gun fires a fin-stabilised discarding sabot round with a muzzle velocity of 1700+ m/s and an effective range of 1500/2000m has been reported.
The driver is seated in the front of the hull in the centre whilst the commander is on the right and the gunner on the left of the turret. The fire control system is believed to include a laser rangefinder, ballistic computer, it retains the stabilised sight of the T-62, and the commander can fire the main armament if required.
A schnorkel can be fitted for deep fording operations. A NBC system is provided as is night fighting equipment, the latter includes an infra-red searchlight on the commander's cupola.
Variants
There are no known variants of the T-64/T-72 MBT.
Employment
Russian Army.

Below: *The M-1970 tank which led to the T-64/T-72 MBT*

T-62 Main Battle Tank　　　Soviet Union

Armament: 1 x 115mm smoothbore gun (U-5TS), elevation +17°, depression —4°
1 x 7.62mm PKT co-axial machine gun
40 rounds of 115mm ammunition
3500 rounds of 7.62mm ammunition
Crew: 4
Length: 9.77m (including gun)
6.715m (excluding gun)
Width: 3.352m
Height: 2.40m

G/Clearance: .425m
Weight: 36,500kg
G/Pressure: .72kg.cm²
Engine: Model V-2-62, V-12 water-cooled diesel engine developing 700hp at 2200rpm
Speed: 50km/ph (road)
Range: 480km (road)
Fuel: 1564 litres (total)
Fording: 1.40m

5.486m (with schnorkel)
V/Obstacle: .80m
Trench: 2.80m
Gradient: 60%
Armour: 20mm–170mm

Development/Variants

The T-62 was shown to the public for the first time in May 1965. It is believed to have entered production in 1961/1962 and was developed for the earlier T-54/T-55 series.

The modifications to the earlier T-54/T-55 include a longer and wider hull, a new turret mounted slightly more to the rear, increased track length on the ground, revised turret hatches and no bow or anti-aircraft machine guns.

The T-62 is armed with a 115mm gun that fires fin-stabilised HEAT (m/v 1000 m/s) or HVAP (1400/1600 m/s) rounds, rate of fire is stated as five rounds a minute. The empty cartridge cases are ejected out of a hatch in the turret rear. The gun is longer than that fitted to the T-54 and has a bore evacuator. A laser range-finder may be under development.

The T-62 is fitted with auxilliary external fuel tanks and can also have additional fuel tanks at the rear of the vehicle. It can also lay its own smoke screen from its exhaust pipes either side of the hull. Infra-red fighting and driving lights are fitted, as is an NBC system. Some T-62s have recently been observed fitted with a 12.7mm anti-aircraft machine gun. The T-62 is not manufactured in Poland and Czechoslovakia, as were the earlier T-54s and T-55s.

The T-62 is easily recognisable from the T-54 and T-55 by its longer gun and the wider space between the road wheels.

Employment

Used by Bulgaria, Czechoslovakia, East Germany, Egypt, Hungary, India, Poland, Romania, Soviet Union, Syria, Afghanistan, Iraq, Israel, and Libya.

T-62 Main Battle Tank

T–54 & T–55 Main Battle Tank   Soviet Union

Armament: 1 × 100mm D-10T gun, elevation + 17°, depression −4°
1 × 7.62mm SGMT machine gun co-axial with main armament
1 × 7.62mm SGMT bow machine gun (operated by driver)
1 × 12.7mm DShK anti-aircraft machine gun 34 rounds of 100mm ammunition
500 rounds of 12.7mm machine gun ammunition

3000 rounds of 7.62mm machine gun ammunition
Crew: 4
Length: 9m (including gun)
6.45m (excluding gun)
Width: 3.27m
Height: 2.40m (w/o AA mg)
G/Clearance: .43m
Weight: 36,500kg (loaded)
G/Pressure: .80kg.cm^2

Armour: 20mm–170mm
Engine: V-2-54, V-12, water-cooled diesel developing 520hp at 2000rpm
Speed: 48km/ph (road)
Range: 630km (road)
440km (cross country)
Fuel: 1091 litres (total)
Fording: 1.4m
5.486m (with schnorkel)
V/Obstacle: .80m
Trench: 2.74m
Gradient: 60%

Note. *The range figures include external fuel tanks.*

Development

The T-54 was developed from the earlier T-44 (this is still used for training). The first prototype of the T-54 appeared in 1947 and the first production models in 1949. The first models had a turret that was undercut at the rear and had an external gun mantlet; some of these have seen action in Jordan only six years ago. The 100mm gun is the same as that fitted to the SU-100. The T-54 and T-55 have been manufactured in the Soviet Union, China (under the designation T-59), Czechoslovakia and Poland. The ZSU-57-2 is based on a modified and shortened T-54 chassis.

Variants

T-54: This is the early model with the turret undercut at the rear.
T-54A: This has a bore evacuator, the armament is the D-10TG. Internal modifications include the stabilisation of the main armament in the vertical plane, electric oil pump, bilge pump, improved air filter, infra-red driving equipment, automatic fire extinguishers, additional fuel capacity and power elevation of the main armament.
T-54A(M): This is the T-54 or T-54A fitted with night-fighting equipment, recognisable by the horizontal bracket for the gunner's infra-red searchlight.

T-54B: This model is recognisable by its infra-red searchlight for the tank commander and gunner. The commander's light is on his cupola and the gunner's light has a vertical bracket attached to the right front of the turret. The T-54B can be fitted with a schnorkel; this equipment consists of two pipes which are carried on the rear decking when not required. When assembled they are placed over the loader's turret hatch, where they are supported by wire stays. A much wider pipe is used for training purposes. The The T-54B has the D-10T2S gun which is stabilised in both planes.
T-54C: This is also known as the T-54 (X). The T-54C resembles the T-54B and has a turret dome-shaped ventilator, bracket for the gunner's infra-red searchlight is vertical as in the T-54B. No anti-aircraft machine gun is fitted and a simple hatch replaces the loader's cupola.
T-55 Model 1: This is sometimes known as the T-54C and was first shown to the public in November 1961. It has a horizontal bracket for the gunner's infra-red searchlight, no turret dome ventilator, no anti-aircraft machine gun, a simple hatch for the loader. It has the same D-10T2S gun that is fitted to the T-54B and this is stabilised in both planes; the turret floor rotates. It has a V-55 diesel engine that develops 580hp as well as an improved transmission. It has a total of 43 rounds of 100mm ammunition.
T-55 Model 2: This was first seen in May 1963. It has a raised hatch cover for the loader, smooth metal cover at the base of the commander's cupola, no bow machine gun. Probably has an NBC system.
Mine Clearing Tanks: Both T-54s and T-55s have been modified for mine clearing duties, these being known as PT-54 or PT-55. This equipment consists of various types of wheels mounted in front

Left: *T-54B without anti-aircraft machine gun*

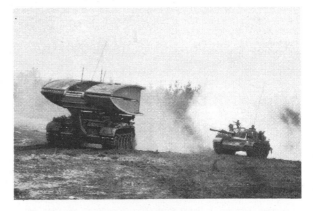

Right: *A T-54 Scissors Bridgelayer*

Right: *A T-54 Armoured Recovery Vehicle Model T-54-T. The large tube on the top of the vehicle is the schnorkel*

Below: *A T-54 with mine-clearing equipment*

of the tank. There are also T-54s fitted with flails for mine clearing operations and turretless versions of the T-54 for the same duties. There is also a new mine-clearing T-55 with a special dozer blade mounted on the front of the vehicle.

Mine Clearing Tanks—Czechoslovakia: Czechoslovakia has developed two types of mine clearing tank. One model is similar to the PT-54 and the other is of the plough type. In the later model there is a plough in front of each track to clear the mines and soil and in addition there is a rake type device between the two ploughs to clear any anti-personnel mines. The Russians have recently developed a mine clearing system similar to the British Giant Viper.

Bulldozer Tanks: Two basic types of bulldozer blade can be fitted. The BTU is used for clearing topsoil and obstacles whilst the STU is used for clearing snow.

Bridgelayer Tank MTU: This is a T-54 with its turret removed. The bridge is carried on the top of the vehicle and winched into position over the obstacle and then lowered down into the desired position. Performance is similar to the basic T-54; some models have been seen with a 12.7mm anti-aircraft machine gun fitted. Basic data is:
Length: 12.30m (with bridge)
Height: 2.865m (with bridge)
Width: 3.27m (with bridge)
Weight: 34,000kg (with bridge)
Bridgelayer Tank M-1967: This is similar to the above bridgelayer except that it has an additional 3.85m on the end of each end of the bridge, these fold on top of the bridge when not in use. The bridge, when opened out, is 20m long and can bridge a gap 19m. The chassis is a T-55.
Bridgelayer Tank MT-55: This has been developed by the Czechoslovakian Army, and is similar to that fitted to their T-34. The vehicle has an NBC system and can have a schnorkel. Opened out, the bridge is 18.2m long.

Amphibious Recovery Vehicle: No firm details are available of this model.
T-54 Flamethrower: Believed to exist, no details are available.
Recovery Vehicle T-54-T: This is a T-54 with its turret removed; a large spade is mounted at the rear of the vehicle; on top of the vehicle is mounted a schnorkel for deep wading. There is another model with no schnorkel and a simple box-like structure. No armament is fitted. Basic data is similar to the T-54 except:
Length: 6.475m
Height: 1.89m
Width: 3.27m
Weight: 32,000kg
Recovery Vehicle T-55-T: This is the same as the above but uses a T-55 chassis.
East German Recovery Vehicles: East Germany uses two types of recovery vehicle based on the T-54 chassis. One model is used to recover vehicles whilst the other is used to tow the recovered vehicle. Each has its turret removed, no spade at the rear, a schnorkel can be fitted, there is a push bar at the front, a boom crane can be erected if required. They can also quickly be fitted with mine-clearing rollers.
Indian T-54s and T-55s: It is reported that some Indian T-54s and T-55s have been rearmed with Russian 115mm guns and have had their machine guns replaced so that they can fire Indian ammunition.
Employment
Used by Albania, Algeria, Afghanistan, Bulgaria, China, Cuba, Czechoslovakia, East Germany, Finland, Egypt, Hungary, India, Israel (see section on Israel), Libya, Mongolia, Morocco, North Korea, Vietnam, North Yemen, Pakistan (both Russian and Chinese models), Peru, Poland, Romania, South Yemen, Soviet Union, Sudan, Syria, Yugoslavia, Angola, Bangladesh, Iraq, PLA, and Uganda.

T-34/85 Medium Tank   Soviet Union

Armament: 1 × 85mm M1944 (ZIS-S53) gun, elevation +25°, depression −5°
1 × 7.62mm bow machine gun and 1 × 7.62mm anti-aircraft machine gun (DTs or DTMs)
56 rounds of 85mm ammunition
2394 rounds of 7.62mm ammunition
Crew: 5
Length: 8.076m (including gun)
6.19m (excluding gun)
Width: 2.997m
Height: 2.743m

G/Clearance: .38m
Weight: 31,750kg (loaded)
G/Pressure: .83kg.cm²
Engine: V-2-34, V-12 diesel, water-cooled developing 500hp at 1800rpm OR V-2-34m V-12 diesel, water-cooled developing 500hp at 1800rpm
Speed: 50km/ph (road)
Range: 354km (road)
Fuel: 773 litres
Note. *Fuel is maximum with external tanks, range includes external tanks.*

A T-34/85 on display at Aberdeen Proving Ground, USA

T-34 Scissors Type Bridgelayer

T-34-C ARV leaving the water

Fording: 1.32m
V/Obstacle: .73m
Trench: 2.50m
Gradient: 60%
Armour: 18mm–75mm

Development

The T-35/85 was developed from the earlier T-34/76 (some of which may still be found in training units) and saw widespread service with the Soviet Army in World War II and was judged by many to be the best tank of the war. The chassis is similar to that used by the SU-85 and SU-100. Postwar the T-34/85 has been in combat in Korea, Hungary, Yemen and Egypt.

Variants

T-34/85 Mineclearing Tanks: There may still be some of these in service; they are fitted with equipment similar to that fitted to the PT-54. Some T-34/85s were fitted with schnorkelling equipment.

T-34/85 Bulldozer Tanks: The vehicle can be fitted with a dozer blade.

SKP-5 Tank Recovery Vehicle: This is a T-34 with its turret removed and fitted with a crane capable of lifting about 5000kg.
Additional data:
Length: 8.00m
Width: 3.00m
Height: 2.60m
Weight: 25,000kg

T-34-T Model A Recovery Vehicle: This is simply a T-34 with no turret and therefore limited to towing operations. Some models have been seen with a superstructure or cupola in place of the turret. Additional data:
Height: 1.70m
Weight: 22,000kg

T-34-T Model B Recovery Vehicle: The equipment fitted to this model includes rigging, jib crane and a platform that can be used to carry engines and transmissions to a maximum weight of 2500kg. Additional data:
Height: 2.14m
Weight: 25,000kg

T-34-T Model C Recovery Vehicle: This model has been developed by Poland and consists of a T-34 chassis with a large armoured superstructure at the front of the vehicle, a bow machine gun is fitted. Additional equipment includes a spade at the rear and a schnorkel for deep wading.

T-34 with Heavy Crane: This has been developed by Czechoslovakia and is also used by Poland. It is basically a T-34 chassis with a heavy hydraulic crane mounted in place of the turret. This crane can lift a maximum of 5900kg, for example a T-54 turret.

T-34 Recovery Vehicle (East German Model): This is also known as the T-34 BG, and is similar to the T-34-T Model B but also has a push-bar on the glacis plate. It also has a winch.

T-34 Bridgelayer (Scissors Type): This is on Czechoslovakian design and it was first seen in 1960. It is a T-34 chassis with a scissors bridge that has a maximum length in position of 22.00m. Additional data is:
Length: 10.00m (with bridge)
Width: 3.20m (with bridge)
Height: 3.70m (with bridge)
Weight: 32,000kg (with bridge)

Egypt SPG: Egypt has some T-34/85s fitted with a 100mm ATG.

Syrian SPG: Syria has some T-34/85s with their turrets removed and replaced by a 122mm D-30 howitzer.

Vietnam SPAAG: Vietnam has some T-34s fitted with a new turret armed with twin 37mm anti-aircraft guns.

Yugoslavian T-34/85: Very few of these were built and none remain in service. They featured a cast turret with a different cupola and a different glacis plate.

Employment

The T-34/85 is still used by Afghanistan, Albania, Algeria, Bulgaria, China, Cuba Cyprus, Czechoslovakia, East Germany, Egypt, Guinea, Hungary, Iraq, Libya, Mali, Mongolia, North Korea, Vietnam, North and South Yemen, Poland, Romania, Somalia, Sudan, Syria, Yugoslavia, Angola, and Bangladesh.

BMD Light Tank/Fire Support Vehicle   Soviet Union

Armament: 1 × 73mm gun
1 × 7.62mm machine gun co-axial with main armament
1 × 7.62mm machine gun in each side of the hull
1 × Sagger ATGW launcher
Crew: 3 + 3/6
Length: 5.3m
Width: 2.65m
Height: 1.85m
Weight: 9000kg
Engine: Diesel

Speed: 50/55km/hr
6 km/hr (water)
Fording: Amphibious
V/Obstacle: .6m
Trench: 2m
Gradient: 60%

Note. *The above data is provisional.*

Development

The BMD was first seen in the military parade held in Moscow in November,

1973, but it is believed to have entered service in 1970/71. The vehicle has a new hull which is not based on any existing vehicle in service with the Red army.

The turret of the BMD is identical to that fitted to the BMP MICV. This is armed with a 73mm smoothbore gun which is fed from an automatic loader, the gun itself has an elevation of +20° and a depression of −5°. The Sagger missiles are reloaded by one of the crew members from within the vehicle. There is a single 7.62mm machine gun mounted in each side of the hull firing forwards.

The personnel compartment is at the rear of the hull and seats between three and six infantrymen, there is no provision for these men to use their weapons from within the vehicle.

The BMD is fully amphibious being propelled in the water by two water jets which are positioned at the rear of the hull, a full range of night vision is provided and it is assumed that the vehicle has a NBC system.

The exact role of the BMD is uncertain at the present time although it is known to have been issued to some Soviet airborne units.

Variants
There are no variants of the BMD.

Employment
In service only with the Red Army.

Above: *The BMD Light Tank/Fire Support Vehicle*

PT–76 Amphibious Light Tank Soviet Union

Armament: 1 × 76.2mm D-56T gun, elevation +30°, depression −4°
1 × 7.62mm SGMT machine gun co-axial with main armament
40 rounds of 76.2mm ammunition are carried
1000 rounds of 7.62mm ammunition are carried
Crew: 3
Length: 7.625m (including gun)
6.910m (excluding gun)
Width: 3.140m

Height: 2.195m
G/Clearance: .37m
Weight: 14,000kg (loaded)
G/Pressure: .48kg.cm²
Engine: V-6, in-line, water-cooled diesel developing 240hp at 1800rpm
Speed: 44km/ph (road)
10km/ph (water)
Range: 260km (road)
Fuel: 250 litres
Fording: Amphibious
V/Obstacle: 1.10m

Trench: 2.80m
Gradient: 70%
Armour: 10mm–15mm

Development

The PT-76 first appeared in 1952 and is a continuation of a long line of Soviet light amphibious tanks. The PT-76 is fully amphibious, being propelled in the water by two water jets at the rear of the vehicle. These are covered when not required. Before entering the water a small trim board is folded forward at the front of the vehicle. The vehicle can lay its own smoke screen if required. The PT-76 chassis, extensively modified in some cases, is used for the following vehicles: ASU-85, BTR-50, OT-62, M-1970, BMP-1, ZSU-23-4, Gainful missile launcher, FROG-2, 3, 4 and 5 tactical missile launchers, GSP amphibious bridging equipment SAM-6, 122mm SPG, PVA tracked amphibian and the Pinguin cross country and arctic survey vehicle, in fact the Pinguin was the basis of the PT-76. Production of the PT-76 has now been completed.

Variants

Model 1: Also known as the Model B. Is armed with the D-56T gun with no bore evacuator and a long multi-slotted muzzle brake.

Model 2: Also known as the Model A. Is armed with the D-56TM gun with a bore evacuator and a double-baffle muzzle brake. The PT-76 Model 2 fitted with a stabilised gun becomes the PT-76B (or Model 4).

Model 3: This has a conventional clean barrel.

Employment

The PT-76 is used by Afghanistan, Bulgaria, China (refer to Chinese section), Cuba, Czechoslovakia, East Germany, Egypt, Finland, Hungary, India, Indonesia, Iraq, Laos (Pathet Lao), North Korea, Vietnam, Pakistan, Poland, Soviet Union, Syria, Yugoslavia Angola, Congo, Israel, and Uganda.

Above: *Russian PT-76 Model 2 Amphibious Tanks show their capabilities*

T–10M Heavy Tank

Soviet Union

Armament: 1 x 122mm gun, elevation +17°, depression −3°, 30 rounds of 122mm ammunition.
1 x 14.5mm KPV machine gun, co-axial with main armament
1 x 14.5mm KPV machine gun, anti-aircraft
1000 rounds of 14.5mm ammunition are carried
Crew: 4
Length: 10.6m (including gun)
7.04m (excluding gun)
Width: 3.566m
Height: 2.43m (w/o A/A machine gun)
G/Clearance: .436m
Weight: 52,000kg
G/Pressure: 0.76kg.cm^2
Engine: V-2-IS, 12 cylinder, water-cooled diesel 700hp at 2000rpm
Speed: 42km/ph (road)
Range: 250km (road)
Fuel: 1180 litres
Fording: 1.2m
V/Obstacle: 0.9m
Trench: 3.00m
Gradient: 60%
Armour: 210mm (maximum)

Note. *The above relates to the T-10M, and fuel includes external tanks.*

The T-10 was developed from the earlier IS-111. The improvements over the IS-111 were a more powerful gun with a bore evacuator, larger turret, improved armour and a more powerful engine. The T-10 is externally distinguishable from the IS-111 by its seven road wheels, larger turret and cut-off corners on the rear hull plate. The T-10 has 12.7mm M1938/46 DShk machine guns.
The T-10M is a modified T-10. These modifications included the fitting of new 14.5mm machine guns, fitting of infra-red driving and fighting equipment. Some T-10Ms have had a metal stowage box welded to the rear of the turrets. It is also reported that the T-10M is fitted with stabilisation equipment for the 122mm gun and can also be fitted with a schnorkel.
The 122mm gun fires HE or APHE rounds, these rounds are of the separate loading type. This accounts for their low rate of fire which is three rounds a minute. The T-10M's barrel has a multi-baffle muzzle brake.

Employment
Bulgaria, Czechoslovakia, East Germany, Egypt, Hungary, Vietnam, Poland, Romania, Soviet Union, Syria.

T-10M Heavy Tank without stowage box on turret rear

IS–111 Heavy Tank

Soviet Union

Armament: 1 x 122mm M1943 gun, elevation +19°, depression −2°
1 x 7.62mm DTM co-axial machine gun
1 x 12.7mm DShk anti-aircraft machine gun
28 rounds of 122mm ammunition
2000 rounds of machine gun ammunition
Crew: 4
Length: 9.83m (including gun)
6.77m (excluding gun)
Width: 3.07m
Height: 2.74m (w/o A/A machine gun)
G/Clearance: .46m
Weight: 46,500kg (loaded)
G/Pressure: .84kg.cm^2
Engine: V-2 IS, V-12 diesel, water-cooled, developing 520hp at 2000rpm
Speed: 37km/ph (road)
Range: 150km (road)
Fuel: 520 litres

Fording: 1.30m
V/Obstacle: 1.00m
Trench: 2.50m
Gradient: 60%
Armour: 20mm–200mm

Development

The IS-111 was developed from the earlier IS-11, this later vehicle is still used for training in the Soviet Union. The improvements over the IS-11 include a new turret without a cupola, the armour arrangement has been improved and a more powerful engine fitted. The IS-111 entered service towards the end of 1945. The IS-IV was a postwar version of the IS-111 and had a co-axial 12.7mm machine gun, additional armour and a more powerful engine. Very few IS-IV were built.

Variants using IS-type chassis:
ISU-122 and ISU-152 Assault Guns: See separate entry.
310mm M-1957 Self-Propelled Gun: This was first shown in November 1957, and is based on a lengthened IS chassis with eight road wheels. The weapon has a range of 22,860m. This weapon is now obsolete.

420mm M-1960 Self-Propelled Mortar: This was also shown in November 1957, and has the same chassis as the above. A modified version was shown in 1960. The weapon has a range of 18,280m. It is now obsolete.
IS-11-T and IS-111-T: Either an IS-11 or IS-111 with its turret removed and stowage boxes fitted to the front of the vehicle. Weight 35,000kg. These are only capable of towing operations.
Scamp ICBM (SS-14): On IS chassis with eight road wheels.
Scrooge ICBM: On IS chassis with eight road wheels.
Scud A and Scud B: Short range missile on IS chassis, six road wheels.
Frog-1: Short range missile on IS chassis, six road wheels, now obsolete.

Employment
IS-11 is still used by China, Cuba and some Warsaw Pact Countries (for training). IS-111 is still used by Bulgaria, Czechoslovakia, East Germany, Hungary, Poland, Romania, Soviet Union, Syria.

Above: *IS-111 Tank*

BRDM-2 Reconnaissance Vehicle   Soviet Union

Armament: 1 × 14.5mm KPVT machine gun, elevation +30°, depression −10° 500 rounds of 14.5mm ammunition 1 × 7.62mm PKT machine gun, co-axial with 14.5mm machine gun
Crew: 4
Length: 5.75m
Width: 2.35m
Height: 2.31m
G/Clearance: .335m
Weight: 7000kg
Armour: 10mm
Engine: GAZ-41, 8 cylinder petrol engine developing 140hp

Speed: 100km/ph (road)
10km/ph (water)
Range: 750km
Fording: Amphibious
V/Obstacle: .4m
Trench: 1.25m
Gradient: 60%
Armour: 10mm

Development/Variants
The BRDM-2 first appeared in 1966 and it is a replacement for the earlier BTR-40P vehicle. The primary role of the vehicle is reconnaissance.

The BRDM-2 is fully amphibious being propelled in the water by a hydrojet at the rear of the vehicle. A trim board is fitted under the nose of the vehicle and this is raised before the vehicle enters the water.

The engine is at the rear of the vehicle and there is a winch at the front. It has four auxiliary wheels, two each side; these are lowered by the driver when required and enable the vehicle to cross trenches. They are driven from a power take-off.

It is fitted with an NBC system and infra-red driving and fighting lights. The turret is the same as that fitted to the BTR-60PB armoured personnel carrier and the Czechoslovakian OT-64 Model 3 armoured personnel carrier.

BRDM-2 (Sagger): This is a basic BRDM-2 with its turret removed and replaced with a launching system for 6 Sagger ATGW. The six Saggers are raised from within the vehicle complete with their overhead armour cover. Data of this model is similar to the basic vehicle except for a height of 2.01m.

BRDM-2 Sam: This was seen for the first time during the Middle East conflict of late 1973. It consists of a BRDM-2 with its turret removed and replaced by four launchers for the SA-7 Strela (or Grail) low-altitude surface to air missile. It is in service with Egypt and Syria. It entered service with the Warsaw Pact Forces, including the Soviet Union in 1972/1973. The second model is the SA-9 which has a total of four missiles in the ready to launch position.

BRDM-2 (Command): This has its turret removed and is also known as the BRDM-2U.

BRDM-2 Rkh: this fulfills a similar role to the BRDM-1 Rkh vehicle and marks lanes through contaminated areas.

Employment

The BRDM-2 is used by Angola, Bulgaria, East Germany, Egypt, Israel, Malawi, PLO, Poland, Romainia, Soviet Union, Syria, and Yugoslavia.

Above: *BRDM-2*

BRDM-1 Series   Soviet Union
Amphibious Reconnaissance Vehicle

Armament: 1 × 7.62mm SGMB machine gun with 1250 rounds AND/OR 1 × 12.7mm DShK machine gun
Crew: 5
Length: 5.70m
Width: 2.25m
Height: 1.90m (w/o armament)
G/Clearance: .315m
Weight: 5600kg (loaded) 5100kg (empty)
Wheelbase: 2.80m
Engine: GAZ-40P, 6 cylinder, in-line, water-cooled petrol engine developing 90hp at 3400rpm
Speed: 80km/ph (road) 9km/ph (water)
Range: 500km
Fording: Amphibious
V/Obstacle: .47m
Trench: 1.22m
Gradient: 60%
Armour: 10mm

Note. *The data relates to the BRDM-1.*

107

Development/Variants

The BRDM-1 was first shown in May 1959. It is used for a variety of roles including command, reconnaissance and radio duties. The vehicle is fully amphibious being propelled in the water by a single waterjet at the rear of the vehicle. This is covered when not required. Before entering the water the trim board is erected at the front of the vehicle, when travelling this is normally kept in the retracted position just under the nose of the vehicle. In addition to the four main wheels there are two sets of small wheels. These are powered and may be lowered as and when required. They enable the vehicle to cross ditches and climb over difficult obstacles. The tyre pressures can be adjusted to suit the ground conditions. A further development of this vehicle is the BRDM-2, for which there is a separate entry. Similar vehicles are the Hungarian FUG-70 and FUG-63 (OT-65).

Above: *BRDM-2*

BRDM-1 (Rkh): This is a specialised vehicle and is used to mark lane lines through chemical and radio-active contaminated areas. On the rear decking of the vehicles are two boxes, each containing 25 markers flags each. These flags are fired into the ground whilst the vehicle is moving. The crew do not have to leave the vehicle.

BRDM-1 with anti-tank missiles:

Model A: This has three SNAPPER (AT-1) anti-tank missiles carried under light armour. When required for launching the overhead doors slide down to each side of the vehicle. The range of the missiles is about 2000m.

Model B: This has three SWATTER (AT-2) anti-tank missiles carried under light armour. When required for launching the overhead doors slide down to each side of the vehicle, as does an armoured cover at the rear. The range of these missiles is about 2400m.

Model C: This is the latest version and carries six SAGGER (AT-3) anti-tank missiles under armour. In this version the six missiles are raised complete with their overhead armour for launching. Effective range is 2500m.

BRDM-1 (Command): This has additional radios and is known as the BRDM-U.

Employment

The above are used by Albania, Bulgaria, Congo, Cuba, East Germany, Egypt, Israel, Poland, Soviet Union, Syria, and Uganda.

Right: *BRDM-1 with no armament fitted*

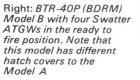

Right: *BTR-40P (BDRM) Model B with four Swatter ATGWs in the ready to fire position. Note that this model has different hatch covers to the Model A*

BA-64 Armoured Car

Soviet Union

Armament: 1 × 7.62mm DTM machine gun
Crew: 2
Length: 3.66m
Width: 1.74m
Height: 1.90m
G/Clearance: .21m
Weight: 2400kg
Wheelbase: 2.13m
Engine: GAZ-MM, 4 cylinder, water-cooled, in-line, petrol engine developing 50hp at 2800rpm
Speed: 80km/ph (road)
Range: 600km
Fording: .47m

V/Obstacle: .40m
Gradient: 60%
Armour: 10mm–15mm

Development/Employment
The BA-64 armoured car was developed during World War II and it is sometimes known as the Bobby. Although it is no longer used by the Russian Army the BA-64 is still used by some satellites including Albania and North Korea. The East German SK-1 armoured car is similar in appearance to the BA-64.

BMP-1

Soviet Union

Mechanised Infantry Combat Vehicle

Armament: 1 × 73mm gun, elevation +20°, depression −5°, 30 rounds of ammunition.
1 × 7.62mm PKT co-axial machine gun
1 × Sagger ATGW launcher rail, with 5 missiles (internal)
Crew: 3 + 8
Length: 6.75m
Width: 3m
Height: 2m
G/Clearance: .40m
Weight: 12,500kg
Armour: 20mm

Engine: Modified V-6, 6 cylinder diesel, 280hp at 2000rpm
Speed: 55km/ph (road)
8km/ph (water)
Range: 300km
Fuel: 300 litres
Fording: Amphibious
V/Obstacle: 1.10m
Trench: 2.00m
Gradient: 60%

BMP-1 of Egyptian Army

Development

The BMP-1 was first shown in 1967 and for a few years was called the M-1967 Armoured Personnel Carrier in the absence of any Soviet designation. The vehicle uses some of the components of the PT-76 but basically it is a new vehicle. The new M-1970 APC does use many components of the BMP-1.

The engine and drive socket are at the front of the vehicle and the rear is taken up by the turret and fighting compartment. There are roof hatches and doors at the rear. The vehicle has a number of interesting features including: fully amphibious being propelled in the water by its tracks; the eight infantrymen can fire their small arms through the firing ports provided (although it must be very cramped). It is fitted with infra-red driving and fighting equipment and also has an NBC system.

The 73mm gun has a short recoil and a low pressure. It fires HEAT rounds and its rate of fire is 8rpm and is fed from a 30 round automatic magazine. The SAGGER ATGW has a range of about 2500m.

Variants

There is believed to be a command version of this vehicle. The Polish Army has a number of vehicles fitted with a smaller gun. There is also an artillery fire control vehicle with a new turret and a radar scanner mounted at the rear.

Employment

In use by: Czechoslovakia, East Germany, Egypt, Iraq, Libya, Poland, Soviet Union, Syria.

BTR-60 PK Armoured Personnel Carrier   Soviet Union

Armament: 1 × 7.62mm SGMB machine gun with 1250 rounds of ammunition
Crew: 2 + 16
Length: 7.56m
Width: 2.825m
Height: 2.06m (w/o machine gun)
G/Clearance: .475m
Weight: 9,980kg (loaded)
Armour: 10mm
Engines: 2 × GAZ-49P, 6 cylinder, water-cooled, in-line, petrol engines developing 90hp at 3400rpm (each)
Speed: 80km/ph (road)
10km/ph (water)
Range: 500km
Fuel: 290 litres
Fording: Amphibious
V/Obstacle: .60m
Trench: 2.00m
Gradient: 60%

Development

The BTR-60P was first shown in November 1961. There are three basic models, details of which are given below. The BTR-60 is an 8 × 8 vehicle, power assisted steering is provided. The vehicle is fully amphibious, being propelled in the water by a single hydrojet at the rear of the vehicle, two smaller jets providing steering. A small trim board is erected before entering the water. The tyre pressures of all eight wheels can be adjusted from a central control to suit current ground conditions. Infra-red driving lights are fitted and later models have infra-red searchlights. Most models are fitted with winches.

Variants

BTR-60P: This was the original open-topped version. Some models have metal hoops over the troop compartment for supporting a canvas cover. The crew are provided with small half-doors in the sides of the vehicle and there are firing ports. Armament consists of a single 12.7mm machine gun and between 1 and 3 7.62mm machine guns, for example one 7.62mm machine gun next to the 12.7mm machine gun at the front and one 7.62mm machine gun either side of the crew compartment.

BTR-60PK: This version has overhead armour and three firing ports either side. It is often called the BTR-60PA. There are at least three versions of this vehicle, each differing slightly in the arrangement of their roof hatches. Armament normally consists of a single 7.62mm or 12.7mm machine gun mounted just behind the front two hatches. The BTR-60PK is fitted with an NBC system.

BTR-60PB: This is a BTR-60PK fitted with a small machine-gun turret mounting a 14.5mm and a 7.62mm machine gun. This turret has a traverse of 360°, and elevation is +30° and depression −10°. The same turret is fitted to the BRDM-2.

Employment

Used by Bulgaria, Cuba, East Germany, Egypt, Iran, Libya, Mongolia, Poland, Rumania, Soviet Union (Army and Marines), Syria, Yugoslavia, Afghanistan, Algeria, Angola, Hungary, Iraq, Israel, North Korea, and Vietnam.

Command: There is a command version called the BTR-60PU and there is also a forward air control model.

Romania: They have built a similar model of the BTR-60PK and this is called the TAB-70, some of these have a 120mm mortar.

Above right: *BTR-60PKs during a parade in Moscow*

BTR-50PK Armoured Personnel Carrier   Soviet Union

Armament: 1 x 7.62mm SGMB machine gun with 1250 rounds of ammunition
Crew: 2 + 20
Length: 7.08m
Width: 3.14m
Height: 1.97m (w/o machine gun)
G/Clearance: .37m
Weight: 14,200kg (loaded)
G/Pressure: .51kg.cm²
Engine: Model V-6, 6 cylinder, in-line, water-cooled diesel developing 240hp at 1800rpm
Speed: 44km/ph (road)
11km/ph (water)
Range: 260km
Fuel: 250 litres
Fording: Amphibious
V/Obstacle: 1.10m

Trench: 2.80m
Gradient: 70%
Armour: 10mm

Development
The BTR-50 was developed from the chassis of the PT-76 light amphibious tank. The vehicle was first seen in 1957. The BTR-50 series are fully amphibious being propelled in the water by two water jets at the rear of the vehicle. Later models of the vehicle are fitted with NBC equipment and infra-red lights. The Czechoslovakian version is called the OT-62, for details of this model refer to the Czechoslovakian section.
Variants
BTR-50P: This was the first model to

enter service and it has an open top, 57mm, 76mm and 85mm anti-tank guns can be carried.

BTR-50PK: This model has overhead protection and is provided with rectangular roof hatches. It has a projecting bay on the left. It has an improved vision device on the right front, and is often fitted with infra-red driving equipment and an infra-red searchlight. One radio aerial is fitted. A new model fitted with the turret of the Czech OT-64 Model 4 has recently been observed.

BTR-50PU Armoured Command Vehicle: This model has overhead protection. There are two models. Model 1 has a projecting bay on the left, Model 2 has two projecting bays. Both Model 1 and Model 2 have a hatch on the left bay, a central rotating cupola just behind the driver, two dome ventilators and two oval-shaped hatches on the roof. There are

normally five radio aerials on the roof. On the Model 2 the right bay has no hatch cover and no infra-red searchlight. The Model 1 has an infra-red searchlight to the right of the driver. Both models have additional stowage boxes on the rear deck.

Employment
Used by Albania, Bulgaria, China, Czechoslovakia, East Germany, Egypt, Finland, Hungary, India, Iran, Vietnam, Poland, Rumania, Somalia, Soviet Union, Syria Yugoslavia, Angola, Afghanistan, Algeria, Libya, Israel, and Sudan.

Above: *BTR-50P with 12.7mm DShK machine gun*

BTR-152V1 Armoured Personnel Carrier   Soviet Union

Armament: 1 × 7.62mm SGMB machine gun with 1250 rounds (or 12.7mm)
Crew: 2 + 17
Length: 6.83m
Width: 2.32m
Height: 2.05m (w/o machine gun)
G/Clearance: .295m
Weight: 8950kg (loaded)
Engine: ZIL-123, 6 cylinder, in-line, petrol engine developing 110hp at 2900rpm
Speed: 75km/ph (road)
Range: 650km
Fuel: 300 litres
Fording: .80m
V/Obstacle: .60m

Trench: .69m
Gradient: 55%
Armour: 8mm–12mm
Development/Variants
BTR-152: The first BTR-152 6 × 6 vehicle appeared in 1950 and was based on the ZIL-151 truck chassis. This was fitted with large single tyres and a more powerful engine. Later models of the BTR-152 used the ZIL-157 chassis. The BTR-152 can be used as an APC, load carrier, 82mm and 120mm mortar carriers, towing vehicles for heavy 160mm mortars or anti-tank guns. A more recent model has been reported with ATGW.

BTR-152V: This is based on the ZIL-157 chassis, fitted with a system enabling the tyre pressures to be regulated to suit the ground conditions. Variants of the BTR-152V are:

BTR-152V1: External air-lines and a winch. Also known as Model B.

BTR-152V2: Internal air-lines, no winch (from BTR-152). Model C.

BTR-152V3: Internal air-lines, winch infra-red driving lights. Model C.

BTR-152K: This is a BTR-152V3 with overhead armour. The increases the height of the vehicle and its loaded weight is 9200kg. There are probably earlier models of this vehicle in service, ie BTR-152V1s that have been fitted with overhead armour. The BTR-152V3 is also known as the Model D, Model 4 or Model 1961.

BTR-152U: This is a BTR-152 converted into the command role. The roof is higher (2.72m) and additional radios have been installed. Loaded weight is 9200kg, armament is not normally fitted.

BTR-152V with twin 14.5mm guns: This is a BTR-152V fitted with twin

14.5mm machine guns in a powered mount with an elevation of + 80° and a depression of − 5°, traverse is 360°. The machine guns are KPV's and have an effective AA range of 1400m. The vehicle weighs 9600kg, height is 2.80m and it has a crew of four. The Egyptians have some BTR-152's fitted with 4 12.7mm MG53s. There is also reported to be an anti-tank model with Sagger ATGWs.

Employment

Albania, Algeria, Bulgaria, Cambodia, China (built in China as the type 56), Congo, Cuba, East Germany, Egypt, Guinea, Hungary, India, Indonesia, Iran, Israel, Mongolia, North Korea, North Yemen, Palestine Liberation Army, Poland, Rumania, Somalia, Soviet Union, Sudan, Syria, Tanzania, Uganda, Yugoslavia, Afghanistan, Ceylon, and Iraq.

Above: BTR-152VI with external air lines

BTR-40 Armoured Personnel Carrier   Soviet Union

Armament: 1 x 7.62mm SGMB machine gun with 1250 rounds of ammunition
Crew: 2 + 8
Length: 5.00m
Width: 1.90m
Height: 1.75m (w/o machine gun)
G/Clearance: .275m
Weight: 5300kg (loaded)
Wheelbase: 2.70m
Engine: GAZ-40, 6 cylinder, in-line,

water-cooled petrol engine developing 80hp at 3400rpm
Speed: 80km/ph (road)
Range: 285km (road)
Fuel: 120 litres
Fording: .80m
V/Obstacle: .47m
Trench: .70m
Gradient: 58%
Armour: 8mm–13mm

Development

The BTR-40 was developed after the end of World War II and entered production in 1951. It is basically a shortened GAZ-63A 4 × 4 chassis with an armoured body. It is fitted with a winch. It is still in use in small numbers by the Soviet Army, its replacement being the BTR-40P (BRDM) vehicle. The BTR-40 is used as an APC and as a command and reconnaissance vehicle.

Variants

BTR-40: This is a basic vehicle and has no roof; it is often known as the Model A. The data above relates to this version. The crew can fire their personal weapons through the firing ports in the sides and the rear of the vehicle. It has side and rear doors.

BTR-40K: This model has overhead armour. This consists of two sets of hinged doors and in some vehicles these overhead doors have been provided with firing ports. The BTR-40K is also known as the Model B and is fitted with tyre pressure regulating system. Weight is 5700kg.

BTR-40 with twin 14.5mm heavy machine guns: This is the basic BTR-40 fitted with twin 14.5mm KPV heavy machine guns in a power operated mount with a traverse of 360°, elevation between −5° and +80°. The guns have an effective AA range of 1400m and can also be used against ground targets. The vehicle weighs 6000kg, has a crew of four, and a height of 2.50m

BTR-40kh: This model is fitted with equipment enabling it to disperse marking pennants in nuclear contaminated areas.

Employment

Used by Albania, Bulgaria, Czechoslovakia, China (also built there as the Type 55 APC), Cuba, East Germany, Egypt, Guinea, Hungary, Iran, Laos, Mali, North Korea, Vietnam, North Yemen, Poland, Somalia, Soviet Union, Sudan, Syria, Tanzania, Uganda, Yugoslavia, Mozambique and the Middle East. Also by Afghanistan, Algeria, Libya, Indonesia, and Yemen.

Above: *BTR-40 Armoured Personnel Carrier*

M-1974 (or SP-74)
Self-Propelled Howitzer

Soviet Union

Armament: 1 × 121.92mm howitzer
Crew: 4–5
Length: 7.3m
Width: 3.004m
Height: 2.42m
Weight: 20,000kg (loaded)

Engine: Model V-6, 6 cylinder in-line diesel developing 240hp at 1800rpm
Speed: 50km/hr
Range: 300km
V/Obstacle: 1.1m

Trench: 3m
Gradient: 60%

Note. *The above data is provisional.*

Development/Variants
The M-1974 122mm self-propelled howitzer was first seen in public during a parade held in Poland in 1974, it is believed to have entered service several years previously. The hull of the M-1974 is based on components of the PT-76 amphibious tank family. The engine and driver are at the front of the hull with the turret to the rear. The latter has a traverse of 360°. The main armament consists of a 122mm howitzer which is believed to be a modified version of the standard 122mm M-1955 (D-74) towed weapon, a fume extractor has been added to the barrel and the double baffle muzzle brake has been retained. The weapon has a maximum range of 21,900m and is not thought to be provided with any automatic loading system; about 40 rounds of ammunition are carried. The howitzer has an elevation of +45° and a depression of −5°.
The M-1974 is probably provided with a NBC system and most are provided with night vision equipment which includes an infra-red searchlight on the commander's cupola.

Employment
In service with Russian and Polish Armies. It is expected that this SPG will enter service with other members of the Warsaw Pact in the near future.

Below: *The 122mm M-1974 Self-Propelled Howitzer*

M-1973
(or SP-73) Self-Propelled Howitzer
Soviet Union

Development/Variants
The M-1973 (or SP 73) is basically a modified SA-4 Ganef chassis with a new turret mounting a modified version of the 152mm (D-20) towed field howitzer. This can fire a HE round to a maximum range of 17,300m, other types of ammunition include APHE and nuclear. No further information is available at the present time.

GMZ Armoured Tracked Minelayer
Soviet Union

This vehicle has the same chassis as the SA-4 Ganef missile system and the M-1973 self-propelled howitzer. It is normally armed with a 14.5mm KPV machine gun. Basic data is: Length 7.5m, width 3.2m, height 2.5m, crew 4 and is powered by a water-cooled diesel engine. No further details are available. A full range of night vision equipment is provided.

M-1970 (GT-T) — Soviet Union
Multi-Purpose Tracked Vehicle

Armament: 1 × 7.62mm machine gun
Crew: 3 + 10
Length: 6.35m
Width: 2.80m
Height: 2.25m
G/Clearance: .35m
Weight: 10,000kg
Engine: IZ-6, 6 cylinder, water-cooled diesel developing 200hp at 1800rpm
Speed: 55km/ph (road)
5km/ph (water)
Range: 400km
Fording: Amphibious
V/Obstacle: 1.10m
Trench: 2.00m
Gradient: 60%
Development/Variants
The M-1970 Multi-Purpose Tracked Vehicle was first seen in 1970 and entered troop service in 1971/1972. The above data is provisional information. The vehicle is believed to be based on the BMP-1, the requirement being for a much cheaper vehicle than the BMP-1. The M-1970 is used for a wide range of roles including towing anti-tank guns, towing mortars and field artillery, armoured personnel carrier, command vehicle, artillery fire control vehicle and cargo carrier.

The driver is on the left side of the vehicle and on the right side is a cupola-mounted 7.62mm machine gun. There are twin doors at the rear of the vehicle and these are provided with firing ports; in addition there are hatches in the roof of the vehicle. The vehicle is amphibious and is propelled in the water by its tracks.

Some GT-Ts have been fitted with a Pork Trough radar system.

Employment
Used by the Soviet Union, Bulgaria.

GT-Ts on exercise in the snow

ISU-122 and ISU-152 Assault Guns — Soviet Union

Armament: 1 × 122mm M1931/44 (A-19S) gun, elevation + 16°, depression − 3°, total traverse 14°
30 rounds of 122mm ammunition
1 × 12.7mm M1938 DShK anti-aircraft machine gun
Crew: 5
Length: 10.06m (including gun)
6.77m (excluding gun)
Width: 3.07m
Height: 2.47m (w/o A/A machine gun)
G/Clearance: .46m
Weight: 45,000kg (loaded)
G/Pressure: .84kg.cm²
Engine: Model V-2 IS, V-12 diesel, water-cooled, developing 520hp at 2000rpm
Speed: 37km/ph (road)
Range: 150km (road)
Fuel: 500 litres
Fording: 1.30m
V/Obstacle: 1.00m
Trench: 2.50m
Gradient: 60%
Armour: 30mm−200mm

Note. *The data above relates to the ISU-122 with 122mm gun A-19S.*

Development/Variants

ISU-122: This was developed in 1943/1944 and was based on a modified IS-11 chassis. The first models were fitted with the D-25S (M1944) gun but later vehicles were armed with the A-19S (M1931/44) gun. The D-25S gun had the higher rate of fire, six rounds a minute, as it had a wedge type breach block. The A-19S has a screw type breech block. The D-25S gun has an elevation of +16° and a depression of −3°, total traverse is 14°. The ISU-122 (D-25S) and the ISU-122 (A-19S) can be distinguished as the D-25S has a double baffle muzzle brake and a thinner barrel, the A-19S has no muzzle brake, a projecting gun tube and a thicker barrel.

ISU-152: This has a similar hull to the ISU-122. It is armed with a 152mm assault gun M1937/44 (ML-20S) which has an elevation of +20°, a depression of −3°, total traverse being 10°. Only 20 rounds of 152mm ammunition are carried. The gun is shorter than those fitted to the ISU-122, total length including gun being 9.05m.

Recovery Vehicles based on ISU chassis

There are five basic models, and all have their guns removed and plated over.

Model A: This is used for the towing role and weighs 41,500kg.

Model B: This is similar to Model A but has a cargo platform and a jib crane. Some models have a spade at the rear and are fitted with a schnorkel for deep wading. Loaded weight is 44,000kg and height 3.00m.

Model C: This is similar to Model B but has a spade. Weight 45,000kg, length 7.825m.

Model D: This is similar to Model C and is capable of being fitted with a schnorkel. There are two bars at the front of the vehicle for pushing damaged tanks. Weight 45,500kg, length 8.325m.

Model E: This is a modified Model C. It has an 'A' frame and a jib crane, loaded weight is 45,500kg. Jordan has a few of these.

Employment

Used by Warsaw Pact Forces including:
ISU-122: Algeria, Bulgaria, China, Czechoslovakia, Vietnam, Poland, Romania.
ISU-152: Algeria, China, Czechoslovakia, Egypt, Poland, Syria, and Iraq.
ARVs: These are used by most Warsaw Pact Forces and countries that have received Soviet aid.

ISU-152 Assault Gun

SU-100 Assault Gun   Soviet Union

Armament: 1 × 100mm M-1944 (D-10S) gun, elevation +17°, depression −2° (post-war SU-100s have a depression of −4°), traverse 16° (total)
34 rounds of 100mm ammunition are carried
Crew: 4
Length: 9.45m (including gun)
6.19m (excluding gun)
Width: 3.05m
Height: 2.45m
G/Clearance: .4m
Weight: 31,611kg (loaded)
G/Pressure: .82kg.cm²
Engine: V-2-34M, 12 cylinder diesel, developing 500hp at 1800rpm OR V-2-3411, 12 cylinder diesel, developing 520hp at 2100rpm
Speed: 55km/ph (road)
Range: 300km
Fuel: 614 litres*
Fording: 1.3m
V/Obstacle: .73m
Trench: 2.5m
Gradient: 60%
Armour: 20mm−110mm
* *Including four external tanks.*

Development/Variants

The SU-100 was developed from the

earlier SU-85. The SU-100 is recognisable from the SU-85 as the latter has a shorter 85mm gun and no commander's cupola on the right of the superstructure. Another wartime vehicle was the SU-122, none of which remain in service. Most SU-85s were converted into SU-100s or ARVs, or used for training.

The 100mm gun of the SU-100 is the same as that fitted to the T-54 MBT and fires the same ammunition as a number of Soviet field and anti-aircraft guns. Many postwar SU-100s have been fitted with an additional stowage box on the right side of the superstructure.

The SU-85 recovery vehicle is designated SU-85-T and is simply a SU-85 with the gun removed and plated over. The SU-100 recovery vehicle is similar to the SU-85-T

and is designated SU-100-T. The SU-85-T is the more common of the two models, both models may be seen with or without winches fitted. There is also a command model of the SU-100. This is similar to the SU-100-T.

There is also a SU-85 with the gun removed and plated over and a hydraulically operated dozer blade mounted on the front.

Employment
Used by Albania, Algeria, Bulgaria, Communist China, Cuba, Czechoslovakia, East Germany, Egypt, Mongolia, Morocco, North Korea, North Yemen, Romania, Soviet Union, Syria, Yugoslavia, and Iraq.

SU-100 Assault Gun

ASU-85 Self-Propelled Anti-Tank Gun   Soviet Union

Armament: 1 × 85mm gun, elevation +15°, depression −4°, total traverse 12°. 40 rounds of ammunition
1 × 7.62mm PKT machine gun, co-axial with 85mm gun
Crew: 4
Length: 8.49m (including gun)
6m (excluding gun)
Width: 2.80m
Height: 2.10m
G/Clearance: .40m
Weight: 14,000kg (loaded)
G/Pressure: .44kg.cm^2
Engine: Model V-6, 6 cylinder, in-line, diesel, developing 240hp at 1800rpm
Speed: 44km/ph (road)
Range: 260km (road)
Fuel: 250 litres
Fording: 1.10m
V/Obstacle: 1.10m
Trench: 2.80m

Gradient: 70%
Armour: 10mm−40mm

Development
The ASU-85 was first shown in May 1962, and uses many components of the PT-76 tank. The ASU-85 is not amphibious. The primary role of the vehicle is anti-tank and it is used by the airborne regiments. Each Soviet airborne regiment has a battery of ASU-85s. This battery has three platoons each with three ASU-85s.

The barrel of the 85mm gun has a fume extractor fitted two-thirds of the way along the barrel, and it is also fitted with a double baffle muzzle brake. This gun fires HE, APHE and HVAP rounds, and its rate of fire is about 3−4 rounds per minute.

The ASU-85 is fitted with infra-red driving and fighting equipment, and recent reports indicate that it may be fitted with more advanced aids for night fighting.

Employment
Used by members of the Warsaw Pact including the Soviet Union, East Germany and Poland.

ASU-85

SU-76 Self-Propelled Gun   Soviet Union

Armament: 1 × 76.2mm M1942/43 gun, elevation + 25°, depression − 5° traverse 20° left and 12° right
60 rounds of 76.2mm ammunition carried
1 × 7.62mm Degtyarev machine gun
Crew: 4
Length: 5m
Width: 2.74m
Height: 2.17m
G/Clearance: .32m
Weight: 11,176kg (loaded)
G/Pressure: .57kg.cm²
Armour: 10mm−25mm
Engines: 2 × GAZ-202, 6 cylinder, in-line, water-cooled petrol engines developing 70hp at 3400rpm (each)
Speed: 45km/ph (road)
Range: 360km (road)
Fuel: 400 litres
Fording: .7m
V/Obstacle: .5m
Trench: 1.4m
Gradient: 60%

Development/Variants
The SU-76 was developed during World War II as a tank destroyer and was based on a lengthened T-70 light tank chassis. The SU-76 was however quickly relegated to the infantry support role as its armour was very thin and the better SU-85 was entering service.

There were a number of slightly different versions of the SU-76: model with the gun in the centre of the vehicle; model with the gun to the left (data above relates to this model). This model could also be seen with a slightly different armour arrangement at the rear, and a model with fully enclosed turret. Some SU-76s were fitted with two GAZ-203 engines of 85hp, these being designated SU-76M. An anti-aircraft version was designated the SU-37. It is now obsolete. The East Germans have modified a number of SU-76s into armoured workshop and recovery vehicles. These modifications include the fitting of a new EM-6 six cylinder diesel developing 120hp at 2000rpm. Armament deleted, external stowage boxes added and internal equipment including a lathe, forge and welding equipment.

Employment
Used by Albania, Communist China, East Germany, North Korea, Vietnam, Yugoslavia.

119

SU-76 Self-propelled gun

ASU-57 Self-Propelled Anti-Tank Gun　　Soviet Union

Armament: 1 × 57mm gun, elevation +12°, depression −5°, total traverse 22° (lightweight model)
1 × 57mm gun gun, elevation +15°, depression −4°, total traverse 12° *(standard model)*
Both carry a 7.62mm machine gun and about 40 rounds of 57mm ammunition
Crew: 3−5
Length: 6.10m (4.995m) (including gun) 3.73m (3.48m) (excluding gun)
Width: 2.21m (2.086m)
Height: 1.46m (cover up) 1.18m (shield down)
G/Clearance: .204m
Weight: 5400kg (3350)kg (loaded)
G/Pressure: .35kg.cm² (lightweight)
Engine: *Standard* − ZIL-123, 6 cylinder, water-cooled, in-line, petrol engine developing 110hp at 2900rpm
Lightweight − M-20E, 4 cylinder water-cooled, in-line, petrol engine developing 55hp at 3600rpm
Speed: 64 (45)km/ph (road)
Range: 320 (250) km
Fording: .70m
V/Obstacle: .50m
Trench: 1.40m
Gradient: 60%
Armour: 6mm

Note. *The data in brackets relates to the light-weight version.*

Development/Variants
The ASU-57 was first shown during the May Day Parade in 1957. It is designed for use by the airborne forces and is therefore readily transportable by aircraft and helicopter. It can be air-dropped. The top side and front armour folds down for transport. There are two basic models of the ASU-57. One is made of standard metal materials and the other is slightly smaller; extensive use of aluminium is made in the latter version.
There are two types of gun used on the ASU-57. Model A has a long thin multi-slotted muzzle brake and uses the Ch-51 gun. Model B has a double baffle muzzle brake and has the Ch-51M gun. The gun fires HE, APHE and HVAP rounds, maximum rate of fire is 6−10rpm.
If required the ASU-57 can carry three infantrymen. The ASU-57 is deployed at battalion level, whilst the ASU-85 is at regimental level.

Employment
The ASU-57 is used by members of the Warsaw Pact Forces including East Germany, Poland and the Soviet Union. It is also used by Yugoslavia, and Egypt.

Top right: *ASU-57*

ZSU-23-4   Soviet Union
Self-Propelled Anti-Aircraft Gun System

Armament: 4 × 23mm automatic cannons, elevation + 80°, depression − 7°, traverse 360°
2000 rounds of 23mm ammunition carried
Crew: 4
Length: 6.30m
Width: 2.95m
Height: 2.25m (w/o radar)
G/Clearance: .40m
Weight: 14,000kg (loaded)
G/Pressure: .48kg.cm^2
Engine: V-6, 6 cylinder, in-line, water-cooled diesel developing 240hp at 1800rpm
Speed: 44km/ph (road)
Range: 260km
Fuel: 260 litres
Fording: 1.07m
V/Obstacle: 1.10m
Trench: 2.80m
Gradient: 70%
Armour: 10mm–15mm

ZSU-23-4 with its radar up

Development/Variants

The ZSU-23-4 anti-aircraft gun system was first seen by the public at the parade held in Moscow on 7th November 1965. The vehicle incorporates many components of the PT-76 tank.

When travelling the large radar scanner folds down behind the rear of the turret. This radar has both acquisition and fire control capabilities and provides information to fire the guns, and the high rate of fire make this an effective weapon. The radar is known as the GUN DISH and picks up aircraft out to a maximum range of 20km. Optical sights are also provided.

Each gun has a cyclic rate of fire of 800 to 1000 rounds per minute, per barrel, although the normal figure is 200 rounds per minute, per barrel. The guns can fire either HEI or API rounds. In the anti-aircraft role the guns have an effective slant range of 2000m. They can also be used against ground targets and would be effective against armoured personnel carriers and soft-skinned vehicles. The ZSU-23-4 is also known as the SHILKA. A similar chassis to that of the ZSU-23-4 is used for the GAINFUL (NATO designation) anti-aircraft missile carrier. This carries a total of three missiles. The GAINFUL is also known as the SA-6 or SAM-6.

Employment

Used by: Bulgaria, Czechoslovakia, East Germany, Egypt, Finland, Hungary, India, Iran, Iraq, Poland, Soviet Union, Syria and Yemen.

ZSU–57–2   Soviet Union
Self-Propelled Anti-Aircraft Gun

Armament: 2 × 57mm anti-aircraft guns
Crew: 6
Length: 8.48m (including guns)
7.42m (excluding guns)
Width: 3.27m
Height: 2.75m

G/Clearance: .425m
Weight: 28,100kg (loaded)
G/Pressure: .63kg.cm^2
Engine: Model V-54, V-12, water-cooled diesel, developing 520hp at 2000rpm
Speed: 48km/ph (road)

Range: 400km (road)
Fuel: 812 litres
Fording: 1.40m
V/Obstacle: .80m
Trench: 2.70m
Gradient: 60%
Armour: 20mm−100mm

Development/Variants
The ZSU-57-2 first appeared in 1957. It consists of a shortened and modified T-54 tank chassis with four road wheels, and is fitted with a turret mounting twin S-68 anti-aircraft guns. The turret has a traverse of 360° and the guns can be elevated from −5° to +85°. The guns are traversed and elevated hydraulically, with hand controls for use in an emergency.

A total of 316 rounds of ammunition are carried of which 264 rounds are ready for immediate use, the ammunition is in clips of four rounds. The empty cartridge cases are ejected into the wire cage on the rear of the turret. The ammunition used is both HE and AP, and are the same rounds as used in the 57mm S-60 anti-aircraft gun. The guns have a maximum rate of fire of 105/120rpm per barrel (cyclic), but practical rate of fire is 70rpm per barrel. The guns can be used against both air and ground targets, against aircraft and practical range is 4000m and in the ground role 3-4000m. An optical fire control system is fitted, although there have been

Left: *The SA-4 (SAM-4) Ganef Surface-to-Air Missile on its mobile tracked launcher. The new Soviet Armoured Tracked Minelayer uses a similar chassis to that used for the SA-4*

Above left: *The SA-9 is based on the BRDM-2 hull. The SA-8 is based on a new 6 × 6 amphibious chassis and was seen in 1975 for the first time*

Above right: *ZSU-57-2*

reports that there is a radar equipped model in service. The vehicle is fitted with infra-red driving equipment and has no capacity for deep wading.
Employment
Used by Bulgaria, Czechoslovakia, East Germany, Egypt, Finland, Hungary, Iran, North Korea, Vietnam, Poland, Romania, Soviet Union, Syria, Yugoslavia, and Iraq.

Below: *The SA-6 (SAM-6) Gainful
Surface-to-Air Missile on its mobile
tracked launcher, this is based on PT-76*
*components. This system was widely
employed by Syrian and Egyptian Forces
during the Middle East War of 1973*

AT-P Armoured Tracked Artillery Tractor   **Soviet Union**

Armament: 1 × 7.62mm SGMT machine
gun
Crew: 3 + 6
Length: 4.45m
Width: 2.5m
Height: 1.83m
G/Clearance: .30m
Weight: 6300kg (loaded)
G/Pressure: .4kg.cm²
Engine: ZIL-123 6 cylinder, in-line, water-
cooled petrol engine developing 110hp at
2900rpm
Speed: 50km/ph
Range: 500km
Fording: .7m
V/Obstacle: .60m
Trench: 1.22m
Gradient: 60%
Armour: 12mm (maximum)

Development/Variants
The AT-P's primary role is one of towing
artillery including 85mm and 100mm anti-
tank guns, 122mm Howitzer D-30 and
anti-aircraft guns. The crew of three consists of a commander, driver and a gunner
for the machine gun which is on the right
of the front superstructure. The rest of the
men are in the rear of the vehicle. The

The AT-P Artillery Tractor

vehicle can also be used as a personnel
carrier or cargo carrier.
Early models of the vehicle have the rear
compartment with no overhead protection,
although a canvas cover could be
erected in bad weather. Later
models have overhead armour protection
and a rear compartment that is the full
width of the vehicle. Some of these later
models have firing/vision ports in the rear
doors. It has been reported that some
vehicles have had the limited traverse

machine gun replaced by a small cupola with all round traverse.

There is a command model called AT-P (Command). This model has overhead protection and a higher cupola for the commander. It is also fitted with fender stowage boxes and the exhaust pipe has been moved from the side to the top of the vehicle. A more recent model has a commander's cupola which can be traversed through 360°

Employment

Used only by members of the Warsaw Pact Forces.

Stridsvagn 103B Main Battle Tank   Sweden

Armament: 1 × 105mm automatic gun with 50 rounds
1 × 7.62mm machine gun on commander's cupola
2 × 7.62mm machine guns on left hull front. 2750 rounds of 7.62mm ammunition are carried
2 × 4 barrelled smoke dischargers and 24 smoke grenades
Crew: 3
Length: 9.80m (including gun)
8.40m (excluding gun)
Width: 3.60m
Height: 2.50m (including machine gun)
2.14m (commander's cupola)
G/Clearance: .50m (maximum)
Weight: 39,000kg (loaded)
Engines: One Rolls Royce K.60 multi-fuel engine developing 240hp at 3750rpm.

One Boeing 553 turbine developing 490shp at 38,000rpm
Speed: 50km/ph (road)
Range: 390km
Fuel: 960 litres
Fording: 1.50m
V/Obstacle: .90m
Trench: 2.30m
Gradient: 60%
G/Pressure: .90kg.cm^2

Strv 103B, note the dozer blade under the hull front, the flotation screen around the hull, and the infra-red driving lights

Development

The STRV.103 (known as the 'S' tank), was first proposed in 1956; feasibity trials were carried out using a Sherman and Ikv.103 chassis. In mid-1958 a contract was awarded to the Bofors company to develop the tank while Volvo developed the power-pack and Landsverk the running gear.

The prototype was completed in 1960. This had no return rollers. After extensive trials a production order was given to Bofors and the first production tank was completed in 1966. The first vehicles built were called the Strv 103A and did not have a floataation screen, other differences included a less powerful turbine. Later models were the Strv 103B. These have the more powerful engine and are fitted with a floatation screen. All Strv 103As have been rebuilt to Strv 103B standards.

The gun is fixed, and aimed in elevation by lowering and raising the road wheels, as the tank has hydro-pneumatic suspension. This gives the gun an elevation of +12° and a depression of −10°. The 105mm gun, which is 11 calibres longer than the British 105mm L7A1 gun, is automatically loaded and can fire APDS, HE or smoke rounds, rate of fire is 10–15 rounds per minute.

Prototypes had a ranging machine gun but this was discarded and it now has an optical rangefinder. A laser rangefinder has been developed.

The tank has a flotation screen permanently mounted under armour. When raised it enables the vehicle to swim at 6km/ph with the aid of its tracks. A bulldozer blade is fitted at the front.

Variants

There are no variants of the Strv 103B although components of the tank are incorporated in the 155mm SPG and the now defunct VEAK 2 × 40mm anti-aircraft gun system. Sweden has started preliminary design work on a new MBT for the 1980's. No further details are available at the present time.

Ikv 91 Light Tank/Infantry Support Vehicle   Sweden

Armament: 1 × 90mm Bofors gun, elevation + 15°, depression − 10°
1 × 7.62mm machine gun, co-axial with main armament
1 × 7.62mm anti-aircraft machine gun on loader's cupola
2 × 6 barrelled smoke dischargers at rear of turret
59 rounds of 90mm ammunition
4500 rounds of 7.62mm ammunition
Crew: 4
Length: 8.83m (including gun)
6.41m (hull only)
Width: 3.00m
Height: 2,36m (overall)
G/Clearance: .40m
Weight: 15,500kg (loaded)
G/Pressure: .45kg.cm²
Engine: Volvo TD 120, 6 cylinder, turbocharged diesel developing 295bhp at 2200rpm

The Ikv 91 Light Tank Infantry/Support Vehicle, note the smoke dischargers on the rear of the turret and the 7.62mm machine gun on the loader's cupola

Speed: 69km/ph (road)
7 km/ph (water)
Range: 550km (road)
Fuel: 405 litres
Fording: Amphibious
V/Obstacle: .80m
Trench: 2.80m
Gradient: 60%

Development/Variants
The contract to develop the IKV 91 (Infanterikanonvagn 91) was awarded to Hägglund and Söner in April 1968. The first of three prototypes 'was completed and assigned to manufacturer's tests in December 1969, and was delivered to the Army in January 1971. The other two prototypes were completed in 1970. After extensive trials a production order was awarded to Hägglund and Söner in March 1972, with production of the vehicle commencing in 1974. The vehicle will replace the Strv 74, Ikv 102 and Ikv 103 vehicles in the Swedish Infantry Brigades and Norrland Brigades.

The vehicle is fully amphibious being propelled in the water by its tracks. A trim vane is erected at the front of the vehicle before entering the water. The hull is of welded construction and the sides of the hull are of the double-plate type. The vehicle is fitted with an NBC system. The vehicle has a speed of 69km/ph at 2200rpm and a maximum speed of 71km/ph at 2450rpm.
The 90mm Bofors low-pressure gun fires fin stabilised HE and HEAT (m/v 825 m/s) rounds, the turret has electro-hydraulic traverse and elevation. The gun is not stabilised in traverse or elevation although provision has been made for this to be installed. Comprehensive sighting and vision equipment which includes a laser rangefinder and a computer is fitted.
Employment
In service with Swedish Army.

Pbv 302 Armoured Personnel Carrier   Sweden

Armament: 1 x 20mm cannon, elevation +50°, depression −10°
2 x 5 smoke grenade launchers
505 rounds of 20mm ammunition
Crew: 2 + 10
Length: 5.35m
Width: 2.86m
Height: 2.50m (including turret)
2.06m (without turret)
G/Clearance: .40m
Weight: 13,500kg (loaded)
G/Pressure: .60kg.cm^2
Engine: Volvo THD 100B, 6 cylinder, in-line, turbo-charged diesel developing 280hp at 2200rpm
Speed: 66km/ph (road)
8km/ph (water)
Range: 300km (road)
Fuel: 285 litres
Fording: Amphibious
V/Obstacle: .61m
Trench: 1.80m
Gradient: 60%

Development
In October 1961 a contract was awarded to AB Hägglund and Söner to develop the Pbv 302 (Pansarbandvagn 302). The first two prototypes were completed in January 1963. After extensive trials a production order was awarded to Hägglund and Söner and the first production vehicle was completed in February 1966. Production of the vehicle was completed in December 1971. Components of the Pbv 302 are used in the Ikv 91, Bgbv 82 and Brobv 941.

The hull is of welded construction and the vehicle is not fitted with an NBC system. The Pbv 302 is fully amphibious being propelled in the water by its tracks. Before entering the water the bilge pumps are switched on and the trim vane erected at the front of the vehicle. The driver, commander and gunner are provided with separate hatches. The crew are provided with separate hatches. The crew are provided with two large doors at the rear of the vehicle in addition to roof hatches; the latter are hydraulically operated and allow the crew to fire their weapons. The gun can be used against both ground and air targets.

Variants
The basic vehicle can be used as an ambulance (carrying 4−8 stretchers), load carrier or armoured recovery vehicle (fitted with a winch in the rear compartment). Other variants are:
Stripbv 3021: Armoured Command Vehicle, has four radios, map boards, tables.
Epbv 3022: Armoured Observation Post Vehicle. This has a driver, gunner, fire control officer and operators. The commander's hatch has been replaced with a large cupola fitted with a combined binocular and rangefinder.
Bplpbv 3023: Armoured Fire Direction Post Vehicle. Battery commander's vehicle, has additional radios and fire direction computer.

Product Improved Pbv 302

This is the basic vehicle modified with the following:

(a) 25mm Oerlikon cannon replacing the 20mm cannon.

(b) Fitting an automatic Allison HT 740 gearbox (trials have taken place with this modification).

(c) Fitting the hydrostatic steering system that has been fitted to the Bgbv 82 and Brobv 941 vehicles.

(d) Fitting the later Volvo THD 100C engine developing 310hp.

(e) Sloping the sides of the vehicle and fitting firing ports and vision blocks so that the crew can aim and fire their weapons from within the vehicle. About eight men would be carried instead of ten.

Employment
In service only with the Swedish Army.

Above: *The Pbv 302 Armoured Personnel Carrier*

155mm Bandkanon 1A Self-Propelled Gun   Sweden

Armament: 1 × 155mm fully automatic gun L/50 with one magazine of 14 rounds. Elevation from −3° to +40°, traverse 15° left and 15° right
1 × 7.62mm anti-aircraft machine gun
Crew: 6
Length: 11.00m (including gun)
6.55m (excluding gun)
Width: 3.37m
Height: 3.85m (including machine gun)
3.35m (w/o machine gun)
G/Clearance: .42m (maximum)
Weight: 53,000kg (loaded)

G/Pressure: .85kg.cm^2
Engines: One Rolls-Royce K.60 multi-fuel engine developing 240hp at 3750rpm. One Boeing 502/10MA gas turbine developing 300shp at 38,000rpm
Speed: 28km/ph (road)
Range: 230km (road)
Fuel: 1445 litres
Fording: 1.00m
V/Obstacle: .95m
Trench: 2.00m
Gradient: 60%
Armour: 10mm–20mm

Development/Variants

The prototype of this vehicle was built in 1960. This differed from the production vehicles in a number of ways, the most noticeable being that it had three return rollers. The first production vehicle was completed in 1966 and production has now been completed. Production was undertaken by Bofors in association with Volvo and Landsverk.

The vehicle incorporates components of the 'S' tank including the powerpack, steering system and hydro-pneumatic suspension.

The gun is fully automatic and has a maximum range of 25,600m and is capable of firing 14 rounds a minute. The magazine holds 14 rounds in two layers of seven. When the ammunition is expended a lorry is brought up with a new magazine. It takes only two minutes to load a new magazine.

The weapon is not fitted with a spade at the rear as its suspension can be locked out when firing, thus poviding a very stable firing platform. No variants have been announced, although when the vehicle was first introduced into service it did not have an anti-aircraft machine gun.

Employment

Used only by the Swedish Army.

Above: 155mm Bandkanon 1A with gun elevated to fire

Bgbv 82 Armoured Recovery Vehicle   Sweden

Armament: 1 × 20mm cannon, elevation + 50°, depression − 10°
8 smoke dischargers mounted either side of turret
Crew: 4
Length: 7.23m
Width: 3.25m
Height: 2.63m (including spades)
2.45m (including turret)
G/Clearance: .45m
Weight: 26,500kg (loaded)
G/Pressure: .82kg.cm²
Engine: Volvo THD 100C, 6 cylinder, in-line, diesel, turbo-charged developing 310hp at 2200rpm
Speed: 56km/ph (road)
8km/ph (water)
Range: 400km (cruising)
Fuel: 550 litres
Fording: Amphibious
V/Obstacle: .60m
Trench: 2.50m
Gradient: 60%

Development/Variants

The Bgbv 82 (Bärgningsbandvagn 82) has been developed and produced by Hägglund and Söner. The prototype was built in 1968 and a total of 24 were built between April and December 1973. The vehicle has a similar chassis to that of the Brobv 941 Bridgelaying Vehicle. The later Ikv 91 uses components of these two vehicles.

The vehicle can be used as a recovery vehicle, towing vehicle (for example it can tow a disabled S tank), replacement of tank components (the loaded weight of 26,500kg includes a spare S tank engine pack), grading and levelling operations and the transportation of equipment.

The Bgbv 82 has a hull of all-welded construction; its side plates are of double-plate type. The front of the vehicle can withstand attack from 20mm ammunition. It is fully amphibious being propelled in the water by its tracks; a flotation screen is erected, trim vane erected and bilge pumps switched on before the vehicle enters the water.

The main winch has a capacity of 20,000kg and has two ranges. The crane has a lifting capacity of 9000kg. There are two anchor spades at the rear of the vehicle and these are hydraulically operated. A hydraulically operated bulldozer blade is fitted at the front of the vehicle and this can be used for both dozing operations and to stabilise the vehicle when the crane or winch is being used.

The vehicle is fitted with infra-red driving lights and there is provision for the fitting of an NBC pack.

Employment

In service with the Swedish Army.

The Bgbv 82 Armoured Recovery Vehicle in travelling order

Brobv 941 Bridgelaying Vehicle   Sweden

Armament: 2 x 7.62mm machine guns
2 x 6 barrelled smoke dischargers
Crew: 4
Length: 17.00m (with bridge)
6.71m (vehicle only)
Width: 4.00m (with bridge)
3.23m (vehicle only)
Height: 3.50m (with bridge)
2.75m (vehicle only)
G/Clearance: .40m
Weight: 29,400kg (with bridge)
22,400kg (without bridge)
G/Pressure: .91kg.cm² (loaded)
Engine: Volvo THD 100C, 6 cylinder, in-
line, turbo-charged diesel developing
310hp at 2200rpm
Speed: 56km/ph (road)
8km/ph (water)
Range: 400km
Fuel: 550 litres
Fording: Amphibious
V/Obstacle: .60m
Trench: 2.50m
Gradient: 60%

Development/Variants
The Brobv 941 (Brobandvagn 941) has
been designed and manufactured by
Hägglund and Söner. It uses the same
basic chassis as the Bgbv 82 Armoured
Recovery Vehicle. The first prototype
Brobv 941 was built in 1968 and production vehicles were delivered to the Swedish
Army in 1973.
The basic role of the vehicle is that of
laying a bridge although it can also transport bridging equipment and can be used
for grading operations.
The vehicle is fully amphibious being propelled in the water by its tracks. The only
preparation required is to switch on the
bilge pumps and lower the trim vane at
the front of the vehicle. The bridge is
towed behind the vehicle when the vehicle
is in the water.
A 15m bridge that weighs 7000kg is
carried; this takes less than five minutes
to place in position and can be taken up
for the other end. The bridge is hydraulically operated. A dozer blade is mounted
at the front of the vehicle, which is used
to stabilise the vehicle when the bridge
is being put into position. It can also be
used to clear river banks so that the bridge
can be correctly positioned.
The bridge has a capacity of 50,000kg.
The bridgelaying mechanism is journalled
in the chassis with two supporting legs
and two hydraulic cylinders. The bridge
is laid and picked up by a telescopic beam
that can be extended to the far pickup
point of the bridge. The Brobv 941 is fitted
with infra-red driving lights and can be
fitted with an NBC pack.
Employment
In service with the Swedish Army.

*Above: The Brobv 941 Bridgelaying
Vehicle in travelling order*

PZ.61 and PZ.68 Main Battle Tank　　　　　　Switzerland

	PZ.61	PZ.68
Crew:	4	4
Length Gun Forward:	9.43m	9.49m
Length Hull:	6.78m	6.9m
Width:	3.06m	3.14m
Height Cupola:	2.72m	2.74m
G /Clearance:	.42m	.40m
Weight Loaded:	38,000kg	39,700kg
Weight Empty:	37,000kg	38,700kg
G /Pressure:	.85kg.cm²	.86kg.cm²
Speed Road:	50km /ph	55km /ph
Range:	300km	300km
Fuel:	760 litres	760 litres
Fording:	1.10m	1.10m
V /Obstacle:	.75m	.80m
Trench:	2.60m	2.60m
Gradient:	70%	70%
Main Armament Calibre:	105mm	105mm
Sec. Armament Calibre:	20mm	7.5mm
A /A Armament Calibre:	7.5mm	7.5mm
Main Armament Elev. /Dep.:	+21°　　−10°	+21°　　−.10°
Smoke Dischargers:	6	6
Ammunition 105mm:	52	52
Ammunition 20mm:	240	—
Ammunition 7.5mm:	3000	5200
Engine:	MB-837 V-8 diesel	MB-837 V-8 diesel
Bhp /rpm:	630 /2200	660 /2200
Armour:	60mm (maximum)	60mm (maximum)

Development

The design of the Pz 61 dates to the early 1950s. Prototypes were constructed in 1958 and 1959 and these were armed with a 90mm gun or a 83.4mm gun (as used in the Centurion at that time). These prototypes were followed by 10 pre-production tanks known as the Pz 58. After extensive trials a development of the Pz 58 was ordered into production. The production model was known as the Pz 61 and was armed with the British 105mm gun as used in late Centurions, Leopard, M-60 and so on. Production started in 1964 and 150 were built at Thun before production was completed in 1966.

In 1968 a further development of the Pz 61 was announced, this being called the Pz 68. After trials a production order for 170 was given and the vehicle entered production at Thun; the first production vehicle was completed in 1971. The improvements of the Pz 68 over the earlier Pz 61 included: 20mm cannon has been replaced by a 7.5mm machine gun, the turret has been modified, the engine develops more power which has increased the road speed, the gun is stabilised so that it has a better chance of hitting an enemy tank when it is firing on the move, it has new tracks with rubber pads. A laser rangefinder is under development. A further order for 110 PZ .68 AA2 has been placed, these will have numerous improvements to the engine, tracks and FCS.

Variants

155m Self-Propelled Howitzer: Under development is the Panzer-Kanone 68. This is based on a PZ 68 hull with a turret mounting a Swiss 155mm howitzer with a traverse of 360°, range of weapon is at least 30,000m. Loaded weight is 47,000kg and road speed 55km /ph. It is also armed with a 7.5mm AA machine gun and six smoke dischargers. It was first shown in 1972.

Bridgelayer: A number of types of bridge have been tested both on the Pz 61 and Pz 68 chassis. The vehicle is called the Brückenpanzer, or Bru. Pz 68 for short.

Armoured Recovery Vehicle: This was developed in 1965 and production vehicles are based on the Pz 68 chassis. It is called the Entpannungspanzer 65. It is designed to recover disabled vehicles, carry out repairs and do minor engineer work. A dozer blade is mounted at the front of the vehicle. 'A' frame can lift 15,000kg, main winch has a capacity of 25,000kg, also has an auxiliary winch and tow bars, tools, etc. Basic data is given below:

Armament: 1 × 7.5mm machine gun and 6 smoke dischargers
Overall Length: 7.60m
Overall Height: 3.25m
Width: 3.15m (including spade)
Width: 3.06m
Weight: 39,000kg (loaded)
Speed: 56km/ph
Crew: 3–5
G/Clearance: .45m

Gradient: 60%
V/Obstacle: .80m
Fording: 1.10m
Trench: 2.50m
Anti-Aircraft Vehicle: This is reported to be under development.
Employment
In service only with the Swiss Army.

Pz 61 Main Battle Tank of the Swiss Army

Left: *The Entpannungspanzer 65 Armoured Recovery Vehicle*

Above: *A modified Pz 68 Main Battle Tank of the Swiss Army*

Mowag Tornado
Mechanised Infantry Combat Vehicle

Switzerland

Armament: 1 × 25mm Oerlikon cannon with an elevation of + 60° and a depression of − 12°
2 × 7.62mm machine guns in single remote controlled mounts
800 rounds of 25mm ammunition
5000 rounds of 7.62mm ammunition
Crew: 3 + 7
Length: 6.05m
Width: 3.15m
Height: 2.94m (top of turret)
1.9m (top of hull)
G/Clearance: .45m
Weight: 20,500kg (loaded)
17,200kg (empty)
G/Pressure: .6 kg/cm²
Engine: MOWAG Model M 8DV-TLK 8 cylinder multi-fuel diesel developing 430hp at 2100rpm
Speed: 70km/hr
Range: 600km (road)
Fuel: 550 litres
Fording: 1.3m
1.8m (with kit)
V/Obstacle: .85m
Trench: 2.2m
Gradient: 60%
Side slope: 40%

Development
The Tornado has been developed by MOWAG Motorwagenfabrik AG of Kreuzlingen as a private venture, the vehicle has been tested by the Swiss and Saudi-Arabian armies but has not yet been placed in production. Its crew consists of the com-mander, driver and gunner, the seven infantrymen are seated at the rear of the vehicle. The 25mm turret has full power traverse through 360°. The two smaller turrets at the rear each have a traverse of 230°, and their machine guns have an elevation of + 60° and a depression of − 15°. Other armament installations are possible, for example the 25mm gun and turret could be replaced by a Marder type turret. There are also two MOWAG designed firing ports in each side of the hull, these allow the crew to fire their weapons from within the hull. The Tornado is provided with a NBC system and a full range of night vision equipment, a deep fording kit has been developed.

Variants
MOWAG have designed a complete range of vehicles using the Tornado chassis including an ARV, ambulance, command vehicle, ATGW vehicle, mortar carrier and an ammunition or load carrier. MOWAG have also built a self-propelled anti-tank gun called the Gepard, this is almost identical to the German Jpz. Kanone. A further development of the Tornado is the Taifun, this has been developed with the assistance of Oto-Melara of Italy.

Employment
Trials.

Top right: *The MOWAG Tornado Mechanised Infantry Combat Vehicle*

134

Mowag Piranha Family   Switzerland

	4 × 4	6 × 6	8 × 8
Crew:	1 + 11	1 + 13	1 + 14
Length:	5.39m	5.97m	6.365m
Width:	2.5m	2.5m	2.5m
Height (hull top):	1.85m	1.85m	1.85m
G /Clearance:	.5m	.5m	.5m
Weight loaded:	7000kg	9800kg	12,300kg
	5850kg	7700kg	8800kg
Speed (road):	100km /hr	100km /hr	100km /hr
Speed (water):	9.5km /hr	10.5km /hr	10.5km /hr
Range:	600km	600km	780km
Fuel litres:	225	200	300
Fording:	Amphibious	Amphibious	Amphibious
V /Obstacle:	.5m	.5m	.5m
Gradient:	70%	70%	70%
Engine type:	Petrol	Diesel	Diesel
Engine hp /rpm:	235 /4000	290 /2800	320 /2800

Development
There are three basic models in the Piranha range, these being a 4 × 4, a 6 × 6 and an 8 × 8, all of these share many common components such as axles, wheels and tyres, suspension, hull front and rear, steering and water propulsion system.

The engine and driver are at the front of the hull with the personnel compartment at the rear. The latter is provided with vision blocks and MOWAG firing ports in the hull sides and rear. The Piranha is fully amphibious being propelled in the water by two propellers; all vehicles are provided with an NBC system.

Variants
4 × 4: This is normally armed with a 7.62mm machine gun which can be aimed

and fired from within the vehicle. It normally carries 11 men plus the driver. Variants include a command vehicle, radio and logistics models.

6 × 6: When used as an armoured personnel carrier it can carry 13 men in addition to the driver. Armament installations available include a 7.62mm machine gun, 20mm cannon, 90mm gun and a 120mm mortar. An 8cm Oerlikon rocket launcher can also be fitted. This model can also be used as an ambulance, command vehicle or radio vehicle. In February, 1977, it was announced that a 6 × 6 version would be built under licence in Canada, this will be known as the Cougar.

8 × 8: This can carry a maximum of 14 men plus the driver. Armament installa-

tions include a 20 or 30mm cannon, twin 30mm anti-aircraft guns, 120mm mortar or an 8cm rocket launcher. In addition a remote controlled 7.62mm machine gun can be mounted on the roof, towards the rear of the vehicle.

Mowag Roland
Armoured Personnel Carrier

Armoured Personnel Carrier
Armament: 1 × 7.62mm machine gun
Crew: 1 + 5
Length: 4.44m
Width: 2.01m
Height: 2.03m (turret top)
1.62m (hull top)
G /Clearance: .4m
Weight: 4700kg (loaded)
3900kg (empty)
Engine: Chrysler eight cylinder petrol engine developing 202hp at 3900rpm.

Employment
Trials complete. Ready for production.

Above: *The MOWAG 4 × 4 Piranha with remote controlled 7.62mm machine gun*

Switzerland

Speed: 110km /hr
Range: 550km
Fording: 1m
V /Obstacle: .4m
Gradient: 60%

Development /Variants
The Roland armoured personnel carrier has

Below: *The MOWAG Roland*

been one of the more successful of the numerous armoured vehicles designed by the MOWAG Company. The vehicle can be adopted to fulfil a wide variety of roles including use as an armoured personnel carrier, internal security vehicle, command and radio vehicle, ambulance or supply carrier. The basic vehicle is armed with a 7.62mm machine gun which can be aimed and fired from within the hull, other armament installations are available however.

Optional equipment for the Roland includes a ventilation system, bullet proof tyres, special firing ports in the hull sides and rear, night vision equipment and an obstacle clearing blade mounted on the front of the hull.

Employment
In service with a number of countries, especially in South America, it is believed that the Roland has been manufactured in Argentina.

Mowag Grenadier Multi-Purpose Vehicle   Switzerland

Armament: See below
Crew: 1 + 8
Length: 4.84m
Width: 2.3m
Height: 2.12m (turret)
1.7m (hull top)
G/Clearance: .4m
Weight: 6100kg (loaded)
4400kg (empty)
Engine: Eight cylinder petrol developing 202hp at 3900rpm
Speed: 100km/hr
9/10km/hr (water)
Range: 550km
Fuel: 180 litres
Fording: Amphibious
V/Obstacle: .4m
Gradient: 60%
Armour: 8mm

Development/Variants
The Grenadier has been designed and built by the MOWAG Company of Kreuzlingen. The vehicle has a hull of all welded steel construction. It is fully amphibious being propelled in the water by a single three bladed propeller at the rear of the hull,

steering in the water is accomplished by two rudders, these being operated by the steering wheel. Two bilge pumps are provided.

When being used as an armoured personnel carrier it can carry a total of nine men including the driver. Other roles include reconnaissance vehicle, ambulance, command and radio vehicle, supply carrier and internal security vehicle. Various armament installations are available including a turret-mounted 20mm cannon, remote controlled 7.62mm machine gun, 8cm multiple rocket launcher; other armament installations are also possible.

Optional equipment includes bullet proof tyres, MOWAG firing ports in the sides and rear of the hull, smoke dischargers, night vision equipment and an air conditioning system.

Employment
Available for production.

Below: *The MOWAG Grenadier with 20mm cannon*

Mowag MR 8-01 Series
Armoured Personnel Carrier

Switzerland

Armament: See text
Crew: 3–5
Length: 5.31m
Width: 2.2m
Height: 2.22m (turret)
1.88m (hull top)
Ground Clearance: .5m (hull)
.3 (axles)
Engine: Chrysler R319 6 cylinder petrol developing 161hp
Weight: 8200kg
Speed: 80km/hr (road)
Wheelbase: 2.60m
Track: 1.95m
Gradient: 60%

Development/Variants
In 1959 the Swiss MOWAG Company sold 20 of these vehicles to the German Border Police. Subsequently production of these was undertaken in Germany by Büssing and Henschel and about 400 were built. The Border Police use two basic models. The first is designated the SW1 (Geschützer Sonderwagen 1) Kfz-91; this has a crew of seven and is not normally armed. The second model is the SW11 (Geschützer Sonderwagen 11) Kfz-91; this has a crew of four and is armed with a turret-mounted 20mm cannon with four smoke dischargers either side of the turret. Some of these vehicles have been transfered to the German Police for use in the internal security role, many of these have been fitted with an obstacle clearing blade at the front of the hull. Other models developed by MOWAG to the prototype stage included the MR 8-09 with a turret-mounted 20mm cannon, MR 8-23 with a 90mm Mecar gun, MR 8-30 with twin 80mm Oerlikon Rocket Launchers; and finally the MR 9-32 which had a slightly different rear hull and carried a 120mm mortar.

Employment
In service in Chile and with the German Police.

Below: *SW1 of the Federal German Border Police*

XM1 Abrams Main Battle Tank   United States

Armament: 1 x 105mm gun
1 x 7.62mm machine gun co-axial with main armament
1 x 12.7mm machine gun on commander's cupola
1 x 7.62mm machine gun on loader's hatch
Crew: 4
Length hull: 7.797m
Width: 3.555m
Height: 2.348m (w/o MGs)
Weight loaded: 52,616kg
G/Pressure: .84kg/cm^2
Engine: Avco-Lycoming AGT 1500HP-C turbine developing 1500hp
Road speed: 72.4km/hr
Cross country speed: 56.32km/hr
Range: 482km
V/Obstacle: 1.066m
Trench: 2.743m
Gradient: 60%

Note. *The above data relates to the prototype, production versions will differ in some detail.*

Development
Following the cancellation of the MBT-70 in 1970, the United States Army went ahead to develop a more austere version called the XM803, but this in turn was cancelled in 1971 owing to rising costs.
The Army then established a task force at the Armor School at Fort Knox, Kentucky, to formulate a concept for a new MBT, this task was completed in January 1973. In June 1973, contracts were awarded to both Chrysler and General Motors to build prototypes of a new tank called the XM1, or Abrams as it later became known. These prototypes were completed and handed over to the Army for trials early in 1976. In November 1976, it was announced that the Chrysler entry had been selected for full scale development. The Army has a total requirement for 3325 XM1 MBTs at a unit cost of $754,000 dollars per tank in 1976 dollars. The tank will not replace all M60s at present in service but will be issued to selected units in the United States and Germany.
Production will commence at the Lima Army Modifications Centre at Lima, Ohio from 1979. Initial production will be at 10 tanks per month but in 1980 this should increase to 30 tanks per month. In the early 1980's a second source will be established at Detroit tank plant when production of the M60 starts to run down.
First production tanks will have the standard 105mm rifled gun, which is the

Below: *One of the prototypes of the Chrysler XM1, note the armoured covers on the suspension*

139

British L7 series gun built in the United States. Later tanks may have a German 120mm smooth bore gun as fitted to the Leopard 2 MBT.

The Germans and Americans have a MOU (Memorandum of Understanding) and under this the Germans may adopt the American engine and FCS, if the Americans adopt the gun and some other components.

Features of the XM1 include its hull and turret which is of the British Chobham armour, fully stabilised main armament, a FCS which includes a Hughes laser range-finder and an improved suspension system. Its gas turbine is said to be far more reliable than conventional engines, is quieter and emits hardly any smoke.

Variants

There are no variants of the XM1 at the present time.

Employment

Entering production for the United States Army.

M–60 Series Main Battle Tank   United States

	M-60	M-60A1	M-60A2
Crew:	4	4	4
Length Gun Forward:	9.309m	9.309m	7.283m
Length Hull Only:	6.946m	6.946m	6.946m
Width:	3.631m	3.631m	3.631m
Height Overall:	3.213m	3.257m	3.20m
G/Clearance:	.463m	.463m	.463m
Weight Loaded:	46,266kg	48,987kg	51,982kg
Weight Empty:	42,184kg	43,999kg	41,459kg
G/Pressure:	.78kg.cm^2	.79kg.cm^2	.76kg.cm^2
Speed Road:	48km/ph	48km/ph	51km/ph
Range Road:	500km	500km	535km
Fuel:	1457 litres	1420 litres	1136 litres
Fording Without Kit:	1.219m	1.219m	1.219m
Fording With Kit:	2.438m	2.438m	2.438m
V/Obstacle:	.914m	.914m	.914m
Trench:	2.59m	2.59m	2.59m
Gradient:	60%	60%	60%
Main Armament Calibre:	105mm	105mm	152mm
Co-Axial MG Calibre:	7.62mm	7.62mm	7.62mm
A/A Armament Calibre:	12.7mm	12.7mm	12.7mm
Ammunition 105mm:	60	63	
Ammunition 7.62mm:	5950	5950	5560
Ammunition 12.7mm:	900	900	1090
Engine:	see below	see below	see below
Armour:	25mm–110mm	25mm–110mm	25mm–110mm

Development

The M-60 was based on the M-48A2 tank and was developed by the Chrysler Corporation. The vehicle entered production at the end of 1959 and entered service in 1960. The vehicle has the 105mm gun as used on the late model Centurion, Leopard, Vickers MBT and Swiss Pz 61 and Pz 68. The first M-60A1 was completed in May 1961, the development designation was M-60E1. The first production M-60A1 was completed in October 1962 and the vehicle is still in production at the Detroit Tank Arsenal which is operated by the Chrysler Corporation.

Both the M-60 and the M-60A1 have a full range of night fighting and night driving aids and have the American type NBC system, a dozer blade can be mounted on the front of the vehicle if required. A kit is available which enables the vehicle to deep ford to a depth of 4.11m. This kit consists of a telescopic tube that fits over the loader's hatch, various parts of the tank are sealed with rubber seals. When not in use the equipment is stowed on th rear of the turret.

Variants

M-60: This is the basic model and has the same turret as the M-48A2. It is powered by a Continental AVDS-1790-2 12 cylinder, air-cooled diesel developing 750hp at 2400rpm. It has three return rollers and no idler tension wheel or fender dust shields. It is armed with the 105mm M-68 in mount M-116, this has an elevation of +19° and a depression of

−10°, a 7.62mm co-axial machine gun M-73 and a 12.7mm anti-aircraft machine gun M-85.

M-60A1: This has a new turret which has more room as well as giving greater ballistic protection. On the rear of the turret is a stowage basket that extends completely around the rear of the turret, the lower portion of the turret is screened. It has no fender dust shields, nor rear idler tension wheels and three return rollers. It is powered by an AVDS-1790-2A which develops 750hp at 2400rpm. It has the same armament as the M-60 except that its 105mm gun is in mount M-140. It also has a more recent fire control system. A laser rangefinder is under development.

M-60A2: This is an M-60A1 hull fitted with a new turret mounting the Shillelagh weapons system. The prototypes were designated M-60A1E1 or M-60A1E2 depending on the vehicle used. Development started in April 1964 and the first prototype was completed in September 1965, although trials were unsuccessful production was ordered in September 1966. The first order was for 300 tanks. By 1971 they had still not entered service. By the end of 1971 the problems had been solved and on 29th November 1971, a contract was signed for retrofit production of 526 M-60A2 tanks along with continued production of the M-60A1. The 152mm tube can fire either the Shillelagh missiles or conventional type rounds. It has an elevation of +20° and a depression of −10°, a total of 46 rounds of ammunition are carried of which 13 can be Shillelagh missiles. The type of ammunition carried does, of course, depend on the tactical situation. Also fitted is a co-axial 7.62mm machine gun, a 12.7mm anti-aircraft gun and smoke dischargers.

M-60A3: This is now in production in the following phases:

Phase 1: This covers an add-on stabilisation system, a top-loading air cleaner and an improved steel track with replaceable track shoes. The new track has twice the life of the old track.

Phase 2: This includes a laser rangefinder, a solid state computer, a tube-over-bar suspension system, a more reliable engine and a new electrical system.

Phase 3: This includes an engine of 900hp, a new transmission, new final drives and an advanced night vision system. This vehicle will have increased performance.

Chrysler 'K' Tank: This was a private venture by the Chrysler Corporation and consists of an M-60A1 with a new turret mounting a long-barrelled 152mm Shillelagh system. It was a project only.

M-60 AVLB: This is similar to the M-48 AVLB except that it uses an M-60 chassis. The bridge can take a load of 60 tons and can span a gap of 18.288m. The bridge takes less than two minutes to lay; the vehicle has a crew of two. Performance is similar to the M-60A1; additional data is:

Length: 11.048m (with bridge)
Width: 4.012m (with bridge)
Height: 4.038m (with bridge)
Weight: 55,746kg (with bridge)
Weight: 41,685kg (vehicle only)
Weight: 14,061kg (bridge only)
M-728 Combat Engineer Vehicle (CEV): This vehicle is based on the M-60A1 chassis and turret; its development designation was T-118E1. The

Above: *An early M-60 Tank of the United States Army*

141

vehicle entered production in 1965 and was issued to the 1st Armoured Division in 1968. The vehicle is designed to destroy enemy positions and fortifications, clear roadblocks and obstacles. Armament consists of a 165mm demolition gun, a 7.62mm co-axial machine gun and a 12.7mm anti-aircraft machine gun. Ammunition carried is 30 rounds of 165mm, 2000 rounds of 7.62mm and 600 rounds of 12.7mm ammunition. An 'A' frame is mounted on the front of the vehicle for lifting operations, a winch with a capacity of 11,340kg is provided. A hydraulically operated dozer blade is also provided. Kits for fording and night operations are available. Performance is similar to the M-60A1; additional data is as follows:

Length: 9.30m (boom erected)
Length: 7.88m (with blade)
Width: 3.70m (with blade)
Height: 3.20m
Weight: 52,163kg (loaded)
Weight: 48,500kg (empty)
Ground Pressure: .86kg.cm^2
Lightweight AVLB Bridge: This is now under development by the US Army mobility equipment R and D centre. Its bridge will span a gap up to 27.432m in width.

Employment

The M-60 and M-60A1 are in service with Austria (M-60A1), Iran, Israel (M-60A1), Italy (200 built in Italy by Oto Melara), Jordan, South Korea, Spain (M-60 AVLB only), Turkey, United States, Ethiopia, Saudi-Arabia, Somalia and Singapore.

Right: *The M-728 Combat Engineer Vehicle is based on the M-60A1*

Right: *The M-60A2*

Top left: *M-60A1 of the Austrian Army. The difference between the M-60 and the M-60A1 can be clearly seen*

Bottom left: *The M60A1 with dozer blade*

Below: *M60A3 MBT*

143

	M-48	M-48A1	M-48A2	M-48A3	M-48A5
Crew:	4	4	4	4	4
Length Gun					
Forward:	8.444m	8.729m	8.686m	7.442m	9.302m
Length Hull:	6.705m	6.870m	6.870m	6.882m	6.870m
Width:	3.631m	3.631m	3.631m	3.631m	3.631m
Height Overall:	3.241m	3.130m	3.089m	3.124m	3.130m
G/Clearance:	.393m	.393m	.387m	.406m	.406m
Weight Loaded:	44,906kg	47,173kg	47,173kg	47,173kg	47,180kg
Weight Empty:	42,240kg	43,999kg	43,999kg	44,452kg	44,460kg
G/Pressure:	.78kg.cm^2	.83kg.cm^2	.83kg.cm^2	.83kg.cm^2	.83kg.cm^2
Speed Road:	42km/ph	42km/ph	48km/ph	48km/ph	48km/ph
Range Road:	112km	112km	260km	470km	390km
Fuel:	757 litres	757 litres	1268 litres	1420 litres	1420 litres
Fording W/O Kit:	1.219m	1.219m	1.219m	1.219m	1.219m
Fording With Kit:	2.438m	2.438m	2.438m	2.438m	2.438m
V/Obstacle:	.915m	.915m	.915m	.915m	.915m
Trench:	2.59m	2.59m	2.59m	2.59m	2.59m
Gradient:	60%	60%	60%	60%	60%
Main Armament					
Calibre:	90mm	90mm	90mm	90mm	105mm
Co-Axial MG:	7.62mm	7.62mm	7.62mm	7.62mm	7.62mm
Anti-Aircraft MG:	12.7mm	12.7mm	12.7mm	12.7mm	12.7mm
Ammunition Main:	60	60	64	62	43
Ammunition Sec.:	5900	5900	5590	6000	5000
Ammunition A/A:	180	500	1365	630	1040
Engine:	See below for details				
Armour:	25mm–110mm for all models				

Development

The M-48 was developed from the earlier M-47. Design work started in 1950 by the Chrysler Corporation and the first pilot model was completed in December 1951 this being designated T-48. Early M-48s used the same engine and transmission as the M-47. In March 1951 additional production lines were established by the Ford Motor Company (they built 900 tanks at Livonia), and the Fisher Body Division of the General Motors Corporation. Production commenced in 1952 and was completed in 1956. The cost of the M-48 and M48A1 programme was some 1249 million dollars. Components of the M-48 are also used in the M-53 and M-55 self-propelled guns and the M-88 ARV. The M-48 was further developed into the M-60 series.

Variants

M-48 and M-48C: This was the first production model and has a small driver's hatch; the commander has a machine gun in an open mount, five return rollers and no idler. The M-48C is similar except that it has a hull of mild steel and is not suitable for combat. The gun has an elevation of +19° and a depression of −9°, this being the same as all M-48 series. The vehicle is powered by a Continental AV-1790-5B,

-7, -7B or -7C, 12 cylinder, air-cooled engine developing 810hp at 2800rpm. It has no fender dust shields and either a 'T' or cylindrical blast deflector on the barrel.

M-48A1: This has a large driver's hatch, a commander's cupola complete with machine gun, fender dust shields, rear track idler wheel and five support rollers, and a 'T' type blast deflector. It is powered by a Continental AV-1790-7C engine developing 810hp at 2800rpm.

M-48A2 and M-48A2C: Development of the M-48A2 started in 1954 and it was designated T-48E2, the prototype was completed in 1955. The improvements over the earlier vehicle included an engine with a fuel-injection system, improved engine deck, constant pressure turret control system, improved fire control system. It could also be fitted with additional fuel tanks which give it a range of 400km. The first production order went to Alco Products of Schenectady, New York, in 1956. A later contract was awarded to Chrysler Delaware Defense Plant (Lenape Ordnance Modification Centre) Newark, Delaware. The main difference between the M-48A2 and the M-48A2C is in vision and fire control equipment, the only visual difference between them is the absence of the track tension idler wheels on the M-48A2C. Both are powered by a Continental AVL-1790-8, 12 cylinder, air-cooled petrol engine developing 825bhp at 2800rpm. Other distinguishing features are three return rollers, raised rear engine covers, stowage basket on the turret rear and a 'T' blast deflector.

M-48A3: Development designation M-48A1E2, this has only three support rollers (although some may be seen with five), no track idler wheel, 'T' blast deflector, fender dust shields. It is powered by a Continental AVDS-1790-2A, 12 cylinder, air-cooled diesel engine developing 750bhp at 2400rpm. It is fitted with infra-red driving and fighting equipment, including a XENON searchlight. Some M-48A3s in Vietnam had revised armament and an improved cupola. Also has improved fire control system and can be fitted with a schnorkel.

M-48A4: The M48A4 programme has been cancelled.

M-48A5: This has many improvements including a 105mm gun as used in the M-60A1, entered service with National Guard in 1976.

M-67: The M-67 was standardised in 1955, development designation was T-67 and a total of 74 were built for the USMC. It is a modified M-48A1. The 90mm gun has been replaced by an M-7-6 flame-thrower gun. This has a slightly shorter tube and is slightly larger in diameter than the standard 90mm tube. The headlamps are slightly lower as the flamethrower has an elevation of +45° and a depression of −12°.

M-67A1: This is an M-48A2 modified for use by the United States Army. It is similar to the above except that it has an M-7A1-6 flame gun.

M-67A2: This is an M-48A3 for use by the USMC. It has the M7A1-6 flame gun with a range of 100–250m depending on the weather conditions.

Note. *At the time of writing none of the flamethrower tanks were in service, they are however held in reserve. They saw extensive service in Vietnam. Basic data of the flamethrower tanks is given below, other data being similar to the basic M-48 tank.*

	M-67	M-67A1	M-67A2
Crew:	3	3	3
Length Gun Forward:	8.23m	8.13m	8.15m
Length Hull:	6.97m	6.87m	6.87m
Width:	3.63m	3.63m	3.63m
Height:	3.13m	3.13m	3.12m
G/Clearance:	.39m	.39m	.39m
Weight Loaded:	47,530kg	47,990kg	48,990kg
Weight Empty:	45,350kg	45,810kg	46,800kg
G/Pressure:	.84kg.cm²	.84kg.cm²	.86kg.cm²
Speed Road:	51km/ph	51km/ph	48km/ph
Range:	160km	260km	470km
Fuel:	763 litres	1268 litres	1420 litres

M-48 AVLB: The M-48 AVLB (Armoured Vehicle Launched Bridge) is based on the hull of the M-48A2. A scissors bridge is fitted. Early M-48 AVLBs were fitted with two machine gun turrets each fitted with a 12.7mm machine gun. Most of these have been removed. The bridge is laid hydraulically and can cross ditches up to 18.29m in width. Additional data is:
Crew: 2
Length: 11.15m
Width: 4.01m
Height: 3.99m
Weight: 58.29 tonnes
Bulldozer: An hydraulic bulldozer blade can be fitted to the M-48 series. The width of the blade is 3.71m and two types of blade are available:

M-8 for the M-48, M-48C and M-48A1; this has a weight of 3.98 tonnes.
M-8A1 for the M-48A2 and other members of the family, weight 3.81 tonnes.

Note. *The M-48 tanks have been updated a number of times in their lives and it is very difficult to distinguish between models.*

Employment
It is in service with Germany (and AVLB), Greece, Israel, Jordan (some have 105mm guns), Norway, Pakistan, South Korea, Vietnam, Spain, Taiwan, Turkey, Thailand, United States (Army and Marine Corps), and Morocco.

Left: *M-48A1 of Greek Army*

Left: *M-48AVLB of German Army*

Below: *M-48A2 of US Army with dozer blade*

M-47 Medium Tank   United States

M-47 of US Army

Armament: 1 x 90mm gun M-36, elevation + 19°, depression − 5°
1 x 7.62mm co-axial machine gun model M-1919A4E1
1 x 7.62mm bow machine gun model M-1919A4E1
1 x 12.7mm anti-aircraft machine gun model M-2
71 rounds of 90mm ammunition
4125 rounds of 7.62mm ammunition
440 rounds of 12.7mm ammunition
Crew: 5
Length: 8.508m (including gun)
6.362m (hull only)
Width: 3.51m
Height: 3.35m (inc. A/A machine gun)
2.95m (w/o A/A machine gun)
G/Clearance: .469m
Weight: 46,170kg (loaded)
42,130kg (empty)
G/Pressure: .935kg.cm²
Engine: Continental AV-1790-5B, 7 or 7B, 12 cylinder, air-cooled petrol engine developing 810bhp at 2800rpm
Speed: 58km/ph (road)
Range: 130km
Fuel: 875 litres
Fording: 1.219m
V/Obstacle: .914m
Trench: 2.59m
Gradient: 60%
Armour: 12.7mm−115mm

Development
The M-47 was developed during the Korean War. It is basically a modified M-46 chassis with a T-42 turret mounting a T-119 gun. The M-46 chassis was given a better cooling system, improved hull armour and different electrical equipment. M-47s were built by the Detroit Tank Arsenal and the American Locomotive Company. M-47s may be seen with two types of blast deflector, one has a 'T' type and the other a cylindrical type.

Variants
M-102 Combat Engineer Vehicle with 165mm gun; none remain in service.
T-66 Flame Thrower Tank: Trials only.
French M-47 with 105mm gun: The French DTAT have fitted an M-47 with the complete gun of the AMX-30 MBT. This would be for export only.
Italian M-47 with 105mm gun: Oto Melara have re-built an M-47 with the 105mm gun of the M-60 as well as fitting the vehicle with the engine, transmission and electrical system of the M-60. This would be for export as the Italian Army has ordered 800 Leopards.
M-47 with Swingfire ATGW: This was shown at the Farnborough Air Display in 1966 and was a proposal only.
M-47 with bridge: The Italian Company of Astra SpA of Piacenza have built a bridge-layer on an M-47 chassis. At the end of each end of the bridge is a ramp that can be used as a pile, thus allowing two bridges to be used.
Korean ARV: The Korean Army have adopted a number of M-47s so that they can be used as ARVs. The gun has been removed and an 'A' frame fitted on the glacis plate with the winch inside of the turret, the rope being taken out through the mantlet where the main gun was fitted.
Spanish M-47 with new engine: Chrysler (Spain) is carrying out a major modification programme which includes the installation of a continental AVDS-1790-2A diesel engine.

Employment
Used by Austria, Belgium (Reserve), Brazil, Greece, Iran, Italy, Jordan, Pakistan, Portugal, Saudi-Arabia, South Korea, Spain, Taiwan, Turkey, Yugoslavia. Japan had some for trials. M-47s are no longer used by the United States or Germany. M-26s are reported to be used by Greece and Turkey.

Sherman Medium Tank   United States

	M-4A1 (WET)	M-4A2 (WET)	M-4A3 (WET)	M-4A3E8
Crew:	5	5	5	5
Length:	7.39m	7.39m	6.273m	7.518m
Width:	2.717m	2.653m	2.667m	2.667m
Height:	3.425m	3.425m	3.374m	3.425m
G/Clearance:	.43m	.43m	.43m	.43m
Weight Loaded:	32,044kg	33,320kg	31,574kg	32,284kg
G/Pressure:	1.02kg.cm^2	1.05kg.cm^2	1.00kg.cm^2	.72kg.cm^2 (wide tracks)
Speed Road:	39km/ph	45km/ph	42km/ph	48km/ph
Range Cruising:	160km	160km	160km	160km
Fuel:	651 litres	560 litres	636 litres	636 litres
Fording:	1.066m	1.016m	.914m	.914m
V/Obstacle:	.609	.609m	.609m	.609m
Trench:	2.286m	2.286m	2.286m	2.286m
Gradient:	60%	60%	60%	60%
Main Armament Cal.:	76mm	76mm	75mm	76mm
Sec. Armament Cal.:	7.62mm	7.62mm	7.62mm	7.62mm
Bow. Armament Cal.:	7.62mm	7.62mm	7.62mm	7.62mm
A/A Armament Cal.:	12.7mm	12.7mm	12.7mm	12.7mm
Ammunition Main:	71	71	104	71
Ammunition 7.62mm:	6250	6250	6250	6250
Ammunition 12.7mm:	600	600	600	600
Elevation:	All have an elevation of +25° and depression −10°			
Engine Type:	R-975-C4	GMC 6046D	Ford GAA	Ford GAA
Bhp/rpm:	400/2400	375/2100	450/2600	460/2600
Armour:	12mm−75mm	12mm−75mm	12mm−75mm	12mm−75mm

Development
The Sherman was devised in the early part of World War II and was built in very large numbers. The above listing is a cross section of typical Shermans that are still in service. The Sherman chassis was used as a basis for a number of other vehicles including the M-7, M-10 and M-36; these have their own pages in this book. For

details of the Israeli Shermans refer to the Israeli section. Other variants in service include:
Recovery Vehicle, Fully Tracked M-32 and M-32A1: Based on a variety of

Argentina still uses the famous Sherman Firefly

chassis including the M-4, M-4A1, M-4A2 and M-4A3. It has an 'A' frame, winch with a capacity of 27.22 tonnes, tools, blocks and so on. The later M-32 has wider tracks (.584m). Basic data is as follows:

Crew: 5
Length Overall: 5.82m
Height: 2.736m
Width: 2.616m
Engine: Continental R-975-C1, 350bhp at 2400rpm
Armament: 1 × 81mm mortar, 1 × 7.62mm bow machine gun, 1 × 12.7mm A/A machine gun
Weight: 28,123kg (loaded)
Speed: 41.8km/ph
Range: 165km

Recovery Vehicle, Full Tracked, Medium M-74: This is a postwar development and is a rebuild based on M-4A3 chassis. Equipment fitted includes a blade at the front, 'A' frame, winch, tools, blocks and so on. Basic data is:

Crew: 4
Length Overall: 7.95m
Height: 3.11m (excluding machine gun)
Width: 3.09m
Weight: 42,525kg (loaded)

Engine: Ford GAA, 8 cylinder petrol 450hp at 2600rpm
Armament: 1 × 3.5in rocket launcher, 1 × 7.62mm bow machine gun and 1 × 12.7mm anti-aircraft machine gun
Fuel: 636 litres
Gradient: 60%
Fording: .91m
V/Obstacle: .61m
Speed: 34km/ph

Sherman Firefly: This was a British modification. A powerful 76.2mm gun replaced the standard gun. No bow machine gun.

Sherman Bridgelayer: Japan has some Shermans with a scissors bridge fitted.

Employment

Shermans are still used by Argentina, Brazil, Chile, Columbia, Guatemala, India, Iran, Israel, Japan, Mexico, Pakistan, Paraguay, Peru, Portugal, Philippines, South Korea, Uganda (from Israel), Yugoslavia. M-32s are still used by Austria, Brazil, Japan, Yugoslavia, Israel and Greece. M-74s are still used by Belgium, Greece, Spain, Turkey, and Yugoslavia. Sherman Firefly is still used by Argentina, Lebanon, Yugoslavia.

Left: *M-74 Armoured Recovery Vehicle of Spanish Army*

Below: *M-32 Armoured Recovery Vehicle of Austrian Army*

M-551 General Sheridan
Light Tank/Reconnaissance Vehicle

United States

Armament: 1 x 152mm launcher M-81, elevation + 19.5°, depression −8°
1 x 7.62mm M-73 co-axial machine gun
1 x 12.7mm M-2 machine gun, commander's cupola
8 grenade launchers, 4 either side of turret
20 conventional rounds, 10 Shillelagh missiles
3000 rounds of 7.62mm ammunition
1000 rounds of 12.7mm ammunition
Crew: 4
Length: 6.299m (overall)
Width: 2.819m
Height: 2.946m (including machine gun)
G/Clearance: .48m
Weight: 15,830kg (loaded)
13,589kg (empty)
G/Pressure: .49kg.cm²
Engine: Detroit Diesel 6V53T, 300hp at 2800rpm
Speed: 70km/ph (road)
5.8km/ph (water)
Range: 600km (road)
Fuel: 598 litres
Fording: Amphibious
V/Obstacle: .838m
Trench: 2.54m
Gradient: 60%

Development
The development of the Sheridan dates back to 1959 and the first prototype, the XM-551, was completed in 1962. Production was undertaken by the Allison Division of the General Motors Corporation at the Cleveland Tank-Automotive Plant. The first production vehicle was completed in June 1966. Production has now been completed, about 1700 having been produced for the American Army.
The M-551 or to give its full title, M-551, Armoured Reconnaissance/Airborne As-sault Vehicle, was developed to replace the M-41 light tank and M-56 SP anti-tank gun, which it has done.
The Sheridan has a number of interesting features including a hull of welded aluminium armour, turret of steel; it is fully amphibious, although a small flexible barrier system is erected around the vehicle before entering the water.
The most interesting part of the Sheridan is its weapons system; this consists of a launcher that can fire Shillelagh missiles, which have a range of some 3000m or a variety of conventional rounds including HEAT and cannister. The Sheridan was deployed to Vietnam where a number of faults showed up. Since then most of the faults have been corrected and the vehicle has now been deployed to Germany. The M-551 has a full range of night driving and fighting aids. In 1971 an 8.3 million dollar contract was awarded to Hughes for the production of a laser rangefinder for the M-551. It was announced in 1976 that a 55 million dollar refit programme was under way for the M-551.

Variants
Numerous variants of the M-551 were projected including missile armed anti-aircraft vehicles, mortar carriers and flamethrower vehicles. A prototype with a scissors bridge has been built, this has a scissors bridge which is 18.28m when opened out. Trials versions include one with a 76mm gun M-41 and another with a 105mm gun.

Employment
In service with the United States Army in the USA and Germany.

M-551 Sheridan, note the ammunition boxes on the sides of the turret

M–41 Light Tank   United States

Armament: 1 × 76mm gun M-32, elevation + 20°, depression − 10°
1 × 7.62mm M-1919A4E1 machine gun, co-axial with 76mm gun
1 × 12.7mm M-2 anti-aircraft machine gun
65 rounds of 76mm ammunition
5000 rounds of 7.62mm ammunition
2175 rounds of 12.7mm ammunition
Crew: 4
Length: 8.212m (including gun)
5.819m (excluding gun)
Width: 3.198m
Height: 3.075 (with machine gun)
2.726m (w/o machine gun)
G/Clearance: .45m
Weight: 23,495kg (loaded)
G/Pressure: .72kg.cm^2
Engine: M-41 and M-41A1, Continental or Lycoming AOS-895-3 M-41A2 and M-41A3, Continental or Lycoming AOS1-895-5, 6 cylinder, air-cooled petrol engine, super-charged, developing 500hp at 2800rpm
Speed: 72km/ph (road)
Range: 161km
Fuel: 530 litres
Fording: 1.06 (without kit)
2.44m (with kit)
V/Obstacle: .711m
Trench: 1.828m
Gradient: 60%
Armour: 12mm–40mm

Development/Variants

The M-41 (development designation T-41 and T-41E1) was a development from the T-37 experimental light tank. The M-41 was manufactured by the Cadillac Division of the General Motors Corporation at Cleveland. The first production M-41 was completed in mid-1951. The M-41 is often called the 'Walker Bulldog'.

The M-41 and M-41A1 are the same except that the M-41A1 has late traversing and elevating mechanism. This gives the tank commander control of both the turret and the guns; in the M-41 the commander has only power control of the turret. The M-41A2 and M-41A3 have the later traversing and elevating mechanism and also the fuel injection engine. Many components of the M-41 are used in the M-42, M-44 and M-52. There were also a number of experimental vehicles on the M-41 chassis, including one with a Sheridan development turret.

The M-41A1s used by Denmark are fitted with an AEG infra-red searchlight type B30A and infra-red sighting device B8V (ELTRO). The QM-41 is a remote controlled model for use in air-surface missile trials.

Employment

The M-41 has been replaced in the United States Army by the M-551 but it is still used by Argentina, Austria, Belgium, Boliva, Brazil, Chile, Denmark, Ecuador, Ethiopia, Japan, Lebanon, Nationalist China, New Zealand, Pakistan, Phillippines, Portugal, Saudi Arabia, Vietnam, Spain, Thailand, Tunisia, Turkey.

M-41 Light Tank of Danish Army with 12.7mm A/A MG and infra-red driving lights

M–24 Chaffee Light Tank   United States

Armament: 1 × 75mm gun M-6, elevation + 15°, depression − 10°
1 × 12.7mm M-2 anti-aircraft machine gun
1 × 7.62mm machine gun, co-axial with main armament
1 × 7.62mm machine gun mounted in bow
Ammunition 48 rounds of 75mm, 440 rounds of 12.7mm and 3750 rounds of 7.62mm
Crew: 4/5
Length: 5.486m (including gun)
5.028m (excluding gun)
Width: 2.95m
Height: 2.77m (including machine gun)
2.46m (commander's cupola)
G/Clearance: .457m
Weight: 18,370kg (loaded)
16,440kg (empty)
G/Pressure: .78kg.cm²
Engines: 2 × Cadillac Model 44T24 petrol, V-8, water-cooled, developing 110hp at 3400rpm (each)
Speed: 55km/ph (road)
Range: 173km (cruising)
Fuel: 416 litres
Fording: 1.02m
V/Obstacle: .91m
Trench: 2.44m
Gradient: 60%
Armour: 10mm–38mm

Development
Development of the M-24 was authorised in March 1943 as the T-24, this became the T-24E1. The first production M-24 was completed in April 1944, production being undertaken by Cadillac and Massey-Harris. The M-24 was the replacement for the M-5 Light Tank and saw action in the last few months of the war in Europe and the Far East. Postwar it has seen extensive action in the Far East with French (Indochina), Cambodian and American (Korea) forces. It was replaced in American service by the M-41.

Variants
The following were built using the M-24 chassis. None of them are known to be in service:
M-19 self-propelled anti-aircraft gun
M-37 self-propelled 105mm gun (howitzer)
M-41 self-propelled 155mm gun (howitzer)
In addition there were numerous trials vehicles, both during and after World War II.
M-24 with 90mm Gun: The French DTAT in association with Thune-Eureka A/S (Norway) have carried out the following modifications to the Chaffee: new French 90mm gun, 12.7 AA and co-axial machine gun, no bow machine gun, General Motors 6V-53T diesel engine, Allison MT 650 gearbox, four smoke dischargers each side of the turret, new tracks and shock absorbers, night fighting devices and so on. This gives the vehicle a much more powerful armament, all weather fighting capability and a higher road range (400km). A total of 54 have been rebuilt in Norway for the Norwegian Army between 1973–76.

Employment
Austria, Cambodia, Ethiopia, Greece, Iran, Iraq, Japan, Laos, Nationalist China, Pakistan, Phillippines, Saudi Arabia, Vietnam, Spain, Thailand, Turkey, Uruguay and Norway.

Below: *Modified M24 of Norwegian Army*

Light Tank M–3A1 and M–5A1

Self-Propelled Howitzer M–8

United States

	M-3A1	M-5A1	M-8
Crew:	4	4	4
Length:	4.53m	4.84m	4.97m
Width:	2.24m	2.25m	2.32m
Height:	2.30m	2.40m	2.30m
G /Clearance:	.42m	.35m	.35m
Weight Loaded:	12,927kg	15,397kg	15,680kg
G /Pressure:	.74kg.cm^2	.88kg.cm^2	.88kg.cm^2
Speed Road:	56km /ph	58km /ph	58km /ph
Range Cruising:	120 /145km	160km	160km
Fuel:	212 litres	310 litres	310 litres
Fording:	.91m	.91m	.91m
V /Obstacle:	.61m	.46m	.46m
Trench:	1.83m	1.62m	1.62m
Gradient:	60%	60%	60%
Main Armament:	37mm	37mm	75mm
Co-Axial Armament:	7.62mm	7.62mm	–
Bow Armament:	7.62mm	7.62mm	–
Anti-Aircraft Armament:	7.62mm	7.62mm	12.7mm
Ammunition Main:	108	147	46
Ammunition 7.62mm:	6890	6500	–
Ammunition 12.7mm:	–	–	400
Engine:	see below	see below	see below
Armour:	10mm–44mm	10mm–54mm	10mm–54mm

Development /Variants

M-3s: The M-3 was developed from the earlier M-2 and saw service with the British Army from 1941. The above data relates to the M-3A1. This was powered either by a Continental W670-9A, 7 cylinder petrol engine developing 250hp at 2400rpm. This gives the tank a range of 120km. Or a Guiberson Model T1020-4, 9 cylinder diesel engine, developing 220hp at 2200rpm. This gives it a range of 145km. In addition to the fuel carried internally an additional 151 litres of fuel could be carried in external jettisonable tanks. The 37mm gun has an elevation of +20° and a depression of −10°. The later M-3A3 had an all-welded hull, increased fuel capacity (386 litres), additional stowage box at the rear, sand shields, additional ammunition stowage. This was made possible as the glacis plate was extended forward and the sponsons lengthened to the rear of the vehicle.

M-5s: Developed from the M-3, the M-5

M3A1 Stuart Light Tank

153

was originally designated M-3 but this was changed to avoid confusion. It was powered by two V-8 Cadillac Series 42 petrol engines developing 110hp at 3200rpm. The later M-5A1 had an improved turret with a radio bulge at the rear and the anti-aircraft gun re-positioned on the right side of the turret.

M-8: This is an M-5 chassis and hull fitted with a new turret mounting a 75mm howitzer with an elevation of +40° and a depression of −20°. The range of the gun was about 8800m. The same turret was fitted to the LVT(A)4.

Employment

M-3s are still used by Bolivia, Brazil, Chile, Dominican Republic, Ecuador, Guatemala, Haiti, Honduras, Indonesia, Mexico, South Korea, Taiwan, Uruguay, Venezuela, Colombia, and Paraquay.

M-5s are still used by Mexico.

M-8s are still used by Mexico.

XR311 High Mobility Wheeled Vehicle United States

Armament: Various machine guns and anti-tank weapons, depending on mission requirements
Crew: 1 + 2
Length: 4.34m
Width: 1.93m
Height: 1.60m
G /Clearance: .28m (minimum)
Weight: 2767kg (loaded)
2087kg (empty, including fuel)
680kg (maximum payload)
G /Pressure: .49kg.cm^2
Engine: Chrysler V-8 petrol 5.2 litres, developing 190hp at 4000rpm
Speed: 130km /ph (road)
90km /ph (10% slope)
10km /ph (60% slope)
Range: 480km (cruising)
Fuel: 98 litres
Fording: .75m
V /Obstacle: .2m
Trench: not applicable
Gradient: 60% +

Development
The primary role of this 4 x 4 vehicle is to provide high-performance combat mobility, both on and off the road. To carry out this role, the vehicle is fitted with power steering, full-time automatic four-wheel drive, four-wheel independent torsion-bar suspension, disc brakes on all wheels, three-speed automatic transmission, centre-mounted transfer gear case with interaxle differential and limited-slip clutch, limited-slip clutches in front and rear differentials, heavy duty shock absorbers, low-pressure tyres and a 5000kg winch at the front of the vehicle. FMC began propriety development of the XR311 in 1969, and completed the first of two prototypes in 1970. The vehicle was demonstrated to the US Army, which resulted in considerable interest. In 1971, the US Army purchased ten second-generation XR 311 prototypes for military potential tests. These vehicles were four anti-armour with the TOW missile system, three reconnaisance vehicles with 12.7mm machine guns and three escort/security vehicles with 7.62mm machine guns and crew armour kits.

The military potential tests were completed in the spring of 1972. Test reports indicated that the XR311 offered unique high-speed cross-country mobility charac-

The FMC XR311 fitted with 7.62mm machine gun

teristics and was particularly suitable for the prescribed missions. Since the FMC has modified the vehicle design.

Because of the highly favourable reactions to date from all test agencies and many officers in the US Army and several other countries, it is anticipated that the XR311 will be adopted world-wide for a variety of roles.

Variants

The vehicle can be quickly fitted out for a variety of roles by installation of special purpose kits:

Anti-Tank: Fitted with the TOW missile launcher system and eight TOW missiles.

Radio: Fitted with ground-to-ground and ground-to-air communications equipment.

Reconnaissance: Armed with 12.7mm machine gun on a ring mount.

Security: Armed with a variety of weapons including 7.62mm machine guns, 40mm grenade launchers, or 7.62mm miniguns.

Other roles could include ambulance, mortar, military police and riot control. A crew compartment armour kit is available, consisting of (1) high-hardness steel doors, side body panels, toe panel, and firewall; and (2) bullet proof windshield and door glass.

Employment

This vehicle has been tested by the United States Army and some are in service with Israeli Army.

Carrier, C & R, M−114
Command and Reconnaissance Vehicle

United States

Armament: 1 × 12.7mm M-2 machine gun with 1000 rounds of ammunition
1/2 × 7.62mm M-60 machine guns with 3000 rounds of ammunition
Crew: 3/4
Length: 4.46m
Width: 2.33m
Height: 2.31m
G/Clearance: .36m
Weight: 6846kg (loaded)
5852kg (empty)
G/Pressure: .35kg.cm²
Engine: Chevrolet Model 283, V-8, OHV, liquid petrol engine developing 160hp at 4650rpm
Speed: 58km/ph (road)
5.4km/ph (water)
Range: 480km (cruising)
Fuel: 416 litres
Fording: Amphibious
V/Obstacle: .51m
Trench: 1.52m
Gradient: 60%

Development/Variants

Development of the M-114 started in 1956. The prototype was the T-114 and this was fitted with a turret-mounted machine gun. The T-114 was classified as limited production in 1961, and standard A in May 1963.

The production vehicles were designated M-114 and these did not have a machine gun turret. Production was undertaken by the Cadillac Division of the General Motors Corporation. The first order was for 1215 vehicles and the first 615 of these were built to M-114 standard, the remainder of the batch were built to M-114A1 standard, as was the

M-114A1 Armoured Command and Reconnaissance Vehicle

second batch of 1295 and the third batch of 1200. The M-114A1 (development designation T-114E1) has a commander's cupola with the single hatch (the M-114 has a two-piece commander's hatch) and electrical firing gear for the 12.7mm machine gun, the machine gun on the M-114A1 can be fired from within the vehicle. Data of the M-114A1 is similar to the M-114 except for weight of 6928kg and a height of 2.33m.

The M-114 is constructed of welded aluminium armour and has torsion bar suspension. It is fully amphibious in the water being propelled by its tracks. Infra-red driving equipment is fitted as is a crew NBC system. Various other weapons have been fitted including the M-139 (20mm Hispano-Suiza HS-820), 90mm turret as fitted to the AML-90 and the TRW 25mm cannon. Early replacement of the M-114 is intended as numerous shortcomings were found when the vehicle was deployed to Vietnam. The M-114 will be phased out of service by 1980 and will be replaced in short term by a modified M-113A1 APC, and in the long term by a special model of the XM723 MICV.

Employment
United States.

Lynx
Command and Reconnaissance Carrier

United States

Armament: 1 × 12.7mm machine gun with 1150 rounds of ammunition
1 × 7.62mm machine gun with 2000 rounds of ammunition
2 × 3 smoke grenade launchers
Crew: 3
Length: 4.597m
Width: 2.413m
Height: 2.171m (including cupola)
1.652m (hull top)
G/Clearance: .406m
Weight: 8775kg (loaded)
7725kg (air-drop)
G/Pressure: .48kg.cm²
Engine: GMC 6V53 diesel, 215hp
Speed: 70.7km/ph (road)
5.6km/ph (water)
Range: 523km
Fuel: 303 litres
Fording: Amphibious
V/Obstacle: 0.61m
Trench: 1.52m
Gradient: 60%
Armour: 38mm (maximum)

Development
The initial vehicle, developed by FMC Corporation as a private venture was called the Command and Reconnaissance Vehicle, C & R. This vehicle is often called the M-113½. The principle suspension and power-train components are the same as the M-113A1 (diesel). The prototype was built in 1963.

The C & R has the commander and driver located side by side. This model was ordered by the Netherlands and the first production vehicle was completed in September 1966.

When Canada purchased the vehicle, they requested certain changes, such as the commander and driver placed in tandem. They named their vehicle Armoured, Full-Tracked, Command and Reconnaissance Carrier, Lynx, the first production vehicle for Canada was completed in May 1968.

The FMC Command and Reconnaissance Carrier of Dutch Army

Both configurations have only four duel road wheels per side, with a hull lower than the M-113, and the engine at the rear. The vehicle is fully amphibious being propelled in the water by its tracks. It has infra-red night driving lights but no NBC system.

Variants
1. Fitted with twin 7.62mm M73 or 7.62mm M37 machine guns in a single cupola.
2. Fitted with a cupola-mounted 20mm cannon, a 7.62mm machine gun being mounted on the front right hatch.
3. At various times it has been proposed to fit small ATGWs in launcher boxes on the roof of the vehicle.

4. A 106mm recoilless rifle mounting is reported to be under development.
5. For trials purposes Rheinmetall have fitted a Netherlands C & R with a turret mounting the Rh 202 20mm cannon.
6. Oerlikon have fitted a Netherlands C & R with a new turret mounting a 25mm cannon and all Netherlands vehicles will be refitted with this turret.
7. Other weapon stations can be incorporated at the time of construction at the discretion of the buyer.
8. Recently FMC have tested a Lynx with a turbocharged diesel and a new tube over bar suspension system.

Employment
Lynx used by Canada.
C & R used by the Netherlands.

M8 Armoured Car and M20 Utility Vehicle

United States

Armament: M8—1 × 37mm gun, 1 × 7.62mm machine gun co-axial with 37mm gun, 1 × 12.7mm anti-aircraft machine gun.
M20—1 × 12.7mm anti-aircraft machine gun.
Ammunition: M8—80 rounds of 37mm, 1500 rounds of 7.62mm and 400 rounds of 12.7mm
M20—1000 rounds of 12.7mm
Crew: 4 (2–6)
Length: 5m
Width: 2.54m
Height: 2.25m (2.31m)
G/Clearance: .29m
Weight Loaded: 7892kg (7937kg)
Engine: Hercules JXD petrol developing 110hp at 3000rpm
Speed: 90km/hr
Range: 560km
Fuel: 212 litres

Fording: .61m
V/Obstacle: .3m
Gradient: 60%
Armour: 3—20mm

Development/Variants M8/M20
The M8 was developed in 1942 by the Ford Motor Company who subsequently undertook production of the vehicle from 1943. The vehicle was built in larger numbers than any other American armoured car. The M20 is basically the chassis and hull of the M8 but with its turret removed and replaced by a super-

Below: *The M8 Greyhound 6 × 6 armoured car*

structure mounting a 12.7mm machine gun on a ring mount. The M8 is also known as the Greyhound.

Employment
Brazil, Cambodia (and M20), Cameroon, Colombia, Congo, Dahomey, Ethiopia, Guatemala, Greece (and M20), Iran (and M20), Laos, Malgasy, Mexico, Morocco, Niger (and M20), Norway, Peru, Saudi-Arabia, Senegal, South Korea, Taiwan, Thailand, Togo, Tunisia, Turkey, Upper Volta, Venezuela and Yugoslavia.

T17E1 Staghound
United States

The T17E1 was built for the British Army by the Chevrolet Company between 1942 and 1943. The vehicle is armed with 37mm gun, co-axial 7.62mm machine gun, 7.62mm anti-aircraft machine gun whilst there is a similar weapon in the hull firing forwards. Total ammunition capacity is 103 rounds of 37mm and 5250 rounds of 7.62mm. Loaded weight is 13,925kg and a crew of five is carried. The T17E2 and T17E3 are no longer in service with any country. British variants were the Staghound II with a 76.2mm howitzer and the Staghound III which had a Crusader tank turret.

Employment
Cuba, Honduras, Lebanon, Rhodesia, Saudi-Arabia and South Africa (Reserve).

Chrysler MAC-1 Armoured Car
United States

Armament: 1 x 20mm turret-mounted cannon, traverse 360°
Crew: 4
Length: 5.26m
Width: 2.44m
Height: 2.11m (including turret)
G/Clearance: .46m (maximum)
Weight: 6710kg (loaded)
Speed: 104km/ph (road)
Range: 480km
Fording: .76m
V/Obstacle: .30m
Gradient: 50%
Engine: Chrysler 361

Development/Variants/Employment
The Chrysler MAC was developed as a private venture by the Chrysler Corporation and a small number were delivered to Mexico in 1963. The vehicle uses a number of standard truck components and is powered by the same engine as the M-113 armoured personnel carrier. It is not amphibious and is capable only of fording. Other Chrysler projects that have not reached prototype stage include a 4 x 4 light armoured car and the 8 x 8 SWAT vehicle.

Commando Multi-Mission Vehicle
United States

	V-100	V-150	V-200
Crew (according to role):	12	12	12
Length:	5.689m	5.689m	6.12m
Width:	2.26m	2.26m	2.438m
Height (over hull):	1.93m	1.95m	1.981m
G/Clearance (axles):	.406m	.381m	.431m
Weight Loaded:	7370kg	9550kg	12,730kg
Weight Empty (basic vehicle curb):	5910kg	6820kg	9298kg
Speed Road:	100km/ph	88km/ph	96km/ph
Speed Water:	4.8km/ph	4.8km/ph	4.8km/ph
Range Road:	965km	965km	600km
Fuel:	303 litres	303 litres	379 litres
Fording:	Amphibious	Amphibious	Amphibious
V/Obstacle:	.609m	.609m	.609m
Gradient:	50%	60%	60%
Engine:	Petrol (200hp)	Petrol (210hp)*	Petrol (275hp)
Track:	1.866m	1.95m	2.038/2.076m
Wheelbase:	2.667m	2.667m	3.263m

Note. *The crew, weight loaded and weight empty depends on the role and type of armament that is fitted. (* or a 155hp diesel engine.)*

Development

The V-100 Commando was developed as a private venture by the Cadillac Gage Company of Warren, Michigan. The first prototype was built in March 1963, and the first production vehicle was built in January 1964. The V-100 was designated XM-706 by the US Army; later this became the M-706. All members of the family are fully amphibious being propelled in the water by their wheels. They are fitted with front mounted winches. All have all-welded hulls, firing ports and vision blocks enabling the crew to fire their weapons from within the vehicle. A wide range of armament systems can be installed, some of which are described below.

Variants

V-100: The following models are available:

(a) Fitted with a turret mounting twin 7.62mm machine guns with 1000 ready rounds and 9000 rounds in reserve, and 12 smoke dischargers.
(b) Fitted with turret-mounted 7.62mm and 12.7mm machine gun, and 12 smoke dischargers.
(c) Fitted with a pod for use in the command/armoured personnel carrier role.
(d) Open topped model on which can be fitted turret, pod, or single 7.62mm machine gun.
(e) Police, rescue, riot control or fire fighting vehicle.
(f) Fitted with TOW missile launcher.
(g) Fitted with turret-mounted 7.62mm minigun.
(h) Fitted with Dragon anti-tank weapons.
(i) 81mm Mortar carrier.
(j) Recovery vehicle.

V-150: This was first shown during 1971 and is designed to fill the gap between the V-100 and the larger V-200. There are four basic versions:

1. Has a crew of two and can carry 10 infantry. Armed with twin 7.62mm machine guns or 1 x 7.62mm and 1 x 12.7mm machine guns, and 12 smoke dischargers.
2. Mortar carrier with a crew of five, armed with an 81mm mortar with 60—80 rounds of ammunition, 7.62mm machine guns and 12 smoke dischargers. 2000 rounds of machine gun ammunition are carried.
3. Armed with a turret-mounted 20mm Oerlikon cannon, a 7.62mm co-axial machine gun and a 7.62mm anti-aircraft machine gun and 12 smoke dischargers. The 20 mm gun has an elevation of + 60° and a depression of −8°. 400 rounds of 20mm and 3000 rounds of 7.62mm ammunition are carried. It has a crew of eight.
4. Armed with a 90mm Mecar gun, a 7.62mm co-axial machine gun, a 7.62mm anti-aircraft machine gun and 12 smoke dischargers. 40 rounds of 90mm and 3000 rounds of 7.62mm ammunition are carried. Crew of four men. Recovery, command and TOW missile versions are also available.

Commando with "A" frame for use in recovery role

Commando armed with a turret-mounted 20mm cannon, co-axial 7.62mm machine gun and 7.62mm Anti-Aircraft machine gun

V-200: This was first shown in 1969 and has been produced in the following roles:
(a) Personnel carrier seating 12 men, armed with 7.62mm machine guns.
(b) Armed with 90mm gun, 7.62mm co-axial machine gun, 7.62mm anti-aircraft machine gun and 12 smoke dischargers.
(c) Armed with a turret-mounted 20mm gun, 7.62mm co-axial machine gun, 7.62mm anti-aircraft machine gun, 12 smoke dischargers. Crew of 11.
(d) Mortar vehicle with 81mm mortar, 7.62mm machine guns and a crew of five.
(e) 120mm mortar carrier, crew of seven and 7.62mm machine guns.
(f) Recovery vehicle, crew of eight, armed with 7.62mm machine guns. Also fitted with an 'A' frame.

Employment
Commandos are used by 22 countries including: Bolivia, Lebanon, Muscat and Oman, Portugal, Somalia, Vietnam, Sudan, United States (Army and Air Force), Ethiopia, Laos, Peru, Saudi-Arabia, Singapore, and Turkey. It is also built in Portugal as the Bravia Ceaimite.

XM723 United States
Mechanised Infantry Combat Vehicle

Armament: 1 x 20mm M-129 cannon with an elevation of + 60° and a depression of − 9°
1 x 7.62mm machine gun co-axial with main armament
600 rounds of 20mm ammunition
3400 rounds of 7.62mm ammunition
Crew: 2 + 8/9
Length: 6.35m
Width: 3.2m
Height: 2.616m (turret roof)
1.981m (hull top)
G/Clearance: .482m
Weight: 19,505kg (loaded)
17,690kg (empty)
G/Pressure: .49kg/cm²
Engine: Cummins VTA-903 water-cooled turbo-charged diesel developing 450hp at 2600rpm
Speed: 72km/hr (road)
7km/hr (water)
Range: 483km
Fuel: 746 litres
Fording: Amphibious
V/Obstacle: .914m

Trench: 2.54m
Gradient: 60%

Development
Since the late 1950s the United States Army has had a requirement for a MICV. Many prototypes were built and tested including the XM-701, XM-734 and the XM-765, but none of these were placed in production. Finally, late in 1972, FMC (who build the M-113 series) were awarded a four year contract to develop a MICV called the XM-723. Prototypes are now being tested and it is anticipated that this should enter production in 1978/79.
The XM-723 has a hull of all welded aluminium construction with additional steel armour to the hull front, sides and rear. The engine, transmission and driver are at the front of the hull, with the personnel compartment at the rear. The latter is provided with firing ports and vision blocks so the crew can fire their weapons from within the hull. Prototypes and early production vehicles will be armed with a 20mm

cannon but a 25mm Bushmaster cannon will be installed from 1980 onwards. The vehicle is fully amphibious being propelled in the water by its tracks, a full range of night vision equipment is provided.
Variants:
The following variants are under development:
(1) Special reconnaissance vehicle to replace the M-114 and the now cancelled ARSV.

(2) Anti-tank vehicle with a new launcher for the TOW missile.
(3) Anti-aircraft vehicle with the French / German Roland SAM, it is most probable however that this missile will be mounted on the M-109 SPG chassis.
Employment
Trials. Not yet in service.

Above: *The XM-723 MICV*

Armoured Infantry Fighting Vehicle (AIFV)

United States

Armament: 1 x 20mm gun, elevation + 60°, depression − 10° OR
1 x 25mm cannon OR
1 x 12.7mm machine gun
1 x 7.62mm co-axial machine gun
600 rounds of 20mm ammunition OR
415 rounds of 25mm ammunition
Crew: 3 + 7
Length: 5.258m
Width: 2.819m
Height: 2.784m (including turret)
2.007m (hull top)
G /Clearance: .432m
Weight: 13,470kg (loaded)
11,292kg (empty)
G /Pressure: .66kg.cm² (loaded)
Engine: Detroit Diesel 6V53T 2-stroke turbo-charged, liquid-cooled diesel engine developing 260hp at 2800rpm
Speed: 61.6km /ph (road)
6.3km /ph (water)
Range: 490km
Fuel: 416 litres
Fording: Amphibious
V /Obstacle: .64m
Trench: 1.68m

Gradient: 60%
Armour: Aluminium and steel

Development /Variants
In 1967, FMC Corporation built two XM-765s for the United States Army. These vehicles used a number of M-113 components and were tested in the USA and Korea. FMC developed this vehicle further as a private venture with the end result being the AIFV, the prototype of which was completed in 1970. The vehicle has been changed and improved in many ways, including additional steel armour attached to the hull (with a gap between it and the aluminium armour), a power-operated weapon station (turret) with a 20mm or 25mm automatic cannon and a co-axial 7.62mm machine gun (currently being designed), five firing ports for individual weapons (two each side and one at the rear), an engine turbo-charger that increases the hp from 215 to 260, and new high-capacity shock absorbers. The vehicle is equipped with the M34 day sight, the M36 day /night sight, or the Philip day /

night sight. The vehicle uses the improved T130E1 track recently adapted for use on the M-113A1. A unique torsion bar and tube suspension system results in superior cross-country performance.

The AIFV is fully amphibious, being propelled in the water by its tracks. It is fitted with infra-red lights for night driving. No NBC system is fitted at present.

Employment
The AIFV is in production for the Netherlands Army, these will be armed with a 25mm Oerlikon cannon.

The FMC Armoured Infantry Combat Vehicle armed with a 12.7mm machine gun

M-113 Series   United States

	M-106	M-106A1	M-113	M-113A1	M-125A1	M-132A1	M-577A1
Crew:	6	6	1 + 12	1 + 12	6	2	5
Length:	4.93m	4.93m	4.87m	4.87m	4.87m	4.87m	4.87m
Width:	2.86m	2.86m	2.69m	2.69m	2.69m	2.69m	2.69m
Width Reduced:	2.54m	2.54m	2.54m	2.54m	2.54m	2.54m	2.54m
Height Overall:	2.50m	2.50m	2.50m	2.50m	2.50m	2.43m	2.68m
Height Reduced:	2.02m	2.02m	2.02m	2.02m	2.02m	2.29m	2.54m
G/Clearance:	.41m	.41m	.41m	.41m	.41m	.41m	.41m
Weight Loaded kg:	11,996	11,865	10,670	10,930	11,140	10,840	11,513
Weight Empty kg:	8790	9010	9210	9470	9035	9475	10,865
G/Pressure kg.cm²:	.57	.57	.52	.54	.55	.54	.57
Speed Road km/ph:	64.4	66.8	64.4	68.4	68.4	68.4	68.4
Speed Water km/ph:	5.6	5.6	5.6	5.8	5.8	5.8	5.8
Range km:	298	475	322	500	483	490	495
Fuel litres:	322	360	322	360	360	360	454
Fording:	AMP	AMP	AMP	AMP	AMP	AMP	AMP
V/Obstacle:	.61m	.61m	.61m	.61m	.61m	.61m	.61m
Trench:	1.68m	1.68m	1.68m	1.68m	1.68m	1.68m	1.68m
Gradient:	60%	60%	60%	60%	60%	60%	60%
Armament MG:	12.7mm	12.7mm	12.7mm	12.7mm	12.7mm	7.62mm	—
Ammunition MG:	2000	2000	2000	2000	2000	2000	—
Engine:	CHRY	GMC	CHRY	GMC	GMC	GMC	GMC

Note. *The Chrysler engine is a Model 75M petrol engine developing 209hp and the GMC engine is a Model 6V53 diesel developing 215hp. Maximum armour is 38mm.*

Development

The M-113 was developed from 1956 by the FMC Corporation who built the earlier M-59 APC. The prototypes were built in 1958 and these were designated T-113E1 and T-113E2. In 1959 a production order was awarded to FMC and by 1960 production was under way. The M-113 is fully amphibious being propelled in the water by its tracks. It is built of welded aluminium armour. The driver is provided with an infra-red periscope for night driving. The vehicle does not have an NBC system. The M-113 was succeeded in production by the M-113A1; this has a diesel engine. The installation of a diesel engine gave a slight increase in speed, but most important of all, a substantial increase in the operating range of the vehicle. By 1976 over 60,000 M-113s and variants had been built in the USA and over 4000 M-113s had been built in Italy by Oto Melara. The M-113A1 has been further developed into the AIFV, for which there is a separate entry. Listed below are the more important variants of the M-113, in addition there are many local variants.

Variants

Mortar Carrier M-106 and M-106A1: The M-106 has a petrol engine and the M-106A1 a diesel engine. It is armed with a 107mm (4.2in) mortar which has a traverse of 90° and fires through a three part circular hatch in the roof. A mortar base and stand are carried externally on the left side of the vehicle enabling the mortar to be fired away from the vehicle. The M-106 carried 93 rounds and the M-106A1 carries 88 rounds of 107mm mortar ammunition. The Swiss have some with 120mm mortars of Swiss design.

Armoured Personnel Carrier M-113 and M-113A1: This is the basic vehicle. In its normal role it carries 12 infantrymen. A wide range of kits are available to adapt it for various roles, these include ambulance, cargo, dozer vehicle, fitters' vehicle, recovery vehicles. It can be fitted with HOT, TOW, ENTAC anti-tank missile systems. Other models in service include the M-113 bridge-layer. This was developed for use in Vietnam and has a bridge that spans a gap up to 10m in width and can carry vehicles of 15,000kg. The ACAV (Armoured Cavalry Assault Vehicle) which is armed with a 12.7mm and two 7.62mm machine guns. Each of these machine guns is protected by an armoured shield. The German and Danish Armies have M-113s modified to carry the British Green Archer mortar locating radar system. The Australians have M-113s with the complete Saladin armoured car turret fitted on the roof of the vehicle. They also have some M-113s with turrets from Commando armoured cars; this turret mounts a 12.7mm and a 7.62mm machine gun. This version is called the M-113A1 Carrier Personnel/Reconnaissance, the Saladin model is known as the M-113A1 (FS) Fire Support Vehicle. A more recent model has a Scorpion turret with 76mm gun. The German Army has a number of M-113s with 120mm mortars.

Mortar Carrier M-125 and M-125A1: This is armed with an 81mm mortar mounted on a baseplate giving the mortar a traverse of 360°. It fires through the the three part circular hatch in the roof, baseplate and stand are carried externally enabling the mortar to be fired away from the vehicle. 114 rounds of 81mm mortar ammunition are carried. First production vehicles were delivered in 1966.

Self-Propelled Flamethrower M-132A1: Prototypes used the M-113 chassis, but production vehicles used the M-113A1 chassis. It is armed with a turret mounting a 7.62mm M-73 machine gun and a M10-8 flame gun; the turret has a traverse of 360° elevation being +55° and depression −5°. The flamethrower has a maximum firing range of 180m and a sustained duration of 32 seconds. Deliveries commenced in 1965, the installation of the turret was carried out by CONDEC of Schenectady, New York. Production was completed in 1967. The vehicle is supported in action by the M-45 (a modified M-548) vehicle. This carries additional fuel for the flame gun.

M-163 Vulcan Air Defence System: This is a Vulcan 20mm cannon mounted on a M-113A1 chassis, the chassis in this case is designated M-741. The Vulcan gun has six barrels and has two rates of fire, 1000 or 3000 rounds per minute, thus allowing it to be used against both ground and air targets. The turret has a traverse of 360°, elevation being +80° and depression −5°. A crew of four is carried. First models were delivered to the Army in August 1968. Also used by Israel.

Command Post M-577 and M-577A1: Both petrol- and diesel-engined models. This is basically an M-113 or an M-113A1 with a higher hull. The vehicle is fitted with additional radios, mapboards, tables and so on; it is also fitted with an NBC system. A tent can be erected at the rear of the vehicle to give additional working space. No armament is fitted. The first production M-577 was completed in 1962.

XM-734 Mechanised Infantry Combat Vehicle: This was basically an M-113 with firing ports in the sides of the vehicle. Trials only.

XM-765 Mechanised Infantry Combat Vehicle: Two of these were built for the US Army in 1967 by FMC. It had firing ports, additional armour and a turret-

mounted gun. It was further developed by FMC into the AIFV.

M-806: This is a recovery vehicle and is provided with a winch in the rear and spades at the rear of the hull.

M-548 Cargo Carrier: Development commenced in May 1963 and the vehicle entered production in 1967. It uses the engine and suspension of the M-113A1 APC. Its role is to carry cargo and ammunition in the battle zone. It is fully amphibious and is armed with a 7.62mm or 12.7mm machine gun. A recovery vehicle was designated XM-696 but this did not enter service.

CHAPARRAL missile carrier: This is an M-548 with four Chaparral surface to air missiles mounted on the rear of the vehicle. It is deployed with the 20mm Vulcan Air Defence System. It entered service in 1968/1969.

HAWK missile carrier: This carries three HAWK surface to air missiles on the rear of the vehicle. These are fired from the vehicle. It is designated M-727.

M-548 (Rapier): This is being developed for Iran by the British Aircraft Corporation and has 8 missiles in the ready-to-launch position.

LANCE system: The Lance missile is carried and fired by the M-752. The chassis was developed from M-113A1 components and is the M-667. Spare missiles are carried by the loader-transporter, the M-688.

Lynx C & R Vehicle: This was developed using components of the M-113. For this vehicle there is a separate entry.

Employment

Argentina, Australia (and M-125A1, M-577A1, M-548), Bolivia, Brazil, Cambodia, Canada (and M-577A1, Lynx,

Top left: *M-113A1 APC*

Centre left: *M-113A1 Armoured Personnel Carrier with dozer blade*

Bottom left: *M-113A1 APC being used in the ambulance role*

Right: *M-113 Fitters' Vehicle, as used by the Australian Army*

Below: *M-577 Command Vehicle*

M-548), Chile, Denmark, Ecuador, Germany, Greece, Iran, Israel (and M-577A1 and M-548), Italy (and M-577), Laos, Lebanon, Libya (from Italy), Netherlands (M-577A1, M-106A1, Lynx), New Zealand, Norway (and M-577), Pakistan, Philippines, South Korea, Vietnam, Spain (and M-577A1, M-125A1, M-548), Switzerland (and M-106, her M-113s are known as Spz-63s), Thailand, Turkey (from Italy), United States, Uruguay, Ethiopia, Guatemala, Haiti, Peru, Somalia, and Taiwan.

Above: *The XM-548E1 with four Chaparral Anti-Aircraft missiles, this system is now known as the M-730*

Left: *M-548 with Rapier SAMs*

Below: *M-106 Mortar Carrier with 107mm mortar*

M—59 Armoured Personnel Carrier   United States

Armament: 1 × 12.7mm M-2 machine gun
2000 rounds of 12.7mm ammunition
Crew: 2 + 10
Length: 5.613m
Width: 3.263m
3.149m (minimum)
Height: 2.387m (including cupola)
2.235m (hull top)
G/Clearance: .457m
Weight: 19,323kg (loaded)
17,916kg (empty)
G/Pressure: .51kg.cm²
Engines: 2 × GMC Model 302, 6 cylinder, water-cooled, in-line, petrol engines developing 127hp at 3350rpm (each)
Speed: 51.50km/ph (road)
6.9km/ph (water)
Range: 164km (road)
Fuel: 518 litres
Fording: Amphibious
V/Obstacle: .46m
Trench: 1.676m
Gradient: 60%
Armour: 16mm

Development
The M-59 was designed and manufactured by FMC. The prototypes were designated T-59 (Cadillac powered) and T-59E1 (GMC powered). The vehicle was in production from February 1954 until March 1959. The whole M-59 programme ran from December 1952 until February 1960 and cost a total of 202 million dollars.
The M-59 is fully amphibious being propelled in the water by its tracks, infra-red driving lights are fitted. There are hatches in the roof and a single ramp at the rear of the vehicle.

Variants
The basic vehicle was armed with a pintle-mounted 12.7mm machine gun; some models were fitted with a cupola-mounted 12.7mm machine gun and these vehicles were known as M-59A1s.
Experimental models of the M-59 included a missile carrier, recoilless rifle carrier and the LVTP-6 amphibious vehicle for the United States Marines.
The basic M-59 could also be used as a load carrier, command vehicle or ambulance.
The M-84 was armed with a 4.2in mortar and had a cupola-mounted 12.7mm machine gun and a crew of six men. The contract for the M-84 ran from May 1956 until May 1958 and a total of 21.7 million dollars was spent on the programme.

Employment
The M-59 has been replaced in the United States Army by the M-113. The vehicle is still in service with Brazil, Greece, Lebanon, Turkey, and Ethiopia.

M-59 Armoured Personnel Carrier being unloaded from a railway wagon

M–75 Armoured Personnel Carrier   United States

Armament: 1 × 12.7mm M-2 machine gun
1800 rounds of 12.7mm ammunition
Crew: 2 + 10
Length: 5.193m
Width: 2.84m
Height: 3.041m (with machine gun)
2.775m (including cupola)
G/Clearance: .457m
Weight: 18,828kg (loaded)
16,632kg (empty)
G/Pressure: .57kg.cm^2
Engine: Continental AO-895-4, 6 cylinder, air-cooled petrol, developing 295hp at 2660rpm
Speed: 71km/ph (road)
Range: 185km
Fuel: 568 litres
Fording: 1.219m
2.032m (with kit)
V/Obstacle: .457m
Trench: 1.67m
Gradient: 60%
Armour: 25mm (maximum)

Development
The M-75 was designed in 1950 by the International Harvester Company. The development designations were T-18, T-18E1 and T-18E2. The vehicle used many components of the M-41 light tank, including the engine and transmission.
The first production M-75 was completed in March 1952 and the last one was built in February 1954. A total of 1729 were built by the International Harvester Company and FMC.
The M-75 was not amphibious which was a drawback, and it was a very expensive

vehicle to build. The vehicle is fitted with infra-red driving lights. The crew were provided with roof hatches and there were two doors at the rear of the vehicle. The M-75 can be recognised from the M-59 and M-113 as the M-75 is much higher.

Variants
There were few minor differences between production batches. Experimental vehicles included the T-64 mortar carrier (with a 4.2in mortar) and a T-73 Infantry Vehicle.

Employment
The M-75 is no longer used by the United States Army although it is used by the Belgian Army.

The M-75 Armoured Personnel Carrier

Armoured Half-Track Vehicles United States

	M-2	M-3	M-3A1	M-4A1	M-9A1	M-16
Crew:	10	13	13	6	10	5
Length Overall:	6.146m	6.34m	6.337m	6.194m	6.32m	6.501m
Width:	2.196m	2.22m	2.22m	2.22m	2.19m	2.159m
Height:	2.26m	2.501m	2.692m	2.26m	2.31m	2.616m
G/Clearance:	.28m	.28m	.28m	.28m	.28m	.28m
Weight Loaded:	8980kg	9072kg	9298kg	9135kg	9348kg	9810kg
Weight Empty:	6940kg	7030kg	6940kg	7144kg	7756kg	8450kg
Speed Road:	73km/ph	73km/ph	73km/ph	73km/ph	73km/ph	64km/ph
Range Road:	242km	321km	321km	321km	321km	250km
Fuel:	227 litres	227 litres	227 litres	227 litres	227 litres	227 litres
Fording:	.812m	.812m	.812m	.812m	.812m	.812m
Gradient:	60%	60%	60%	60%	60%	60%
Armament:	12.7mm		12.7mm		12.7mm	12.7mm(4)
	7.62mm	7.62mm	7.62mm	7.62mm	7.62mm	—
Mortar:	—	—	—	81mm	—	—
Engine:	White	White	White	White	I.H.C.	White
Bhp/rpm:	147/3000	147/3000	147/3000	142/3000	124/3000	142/3000
Armour:	7-13mm	7-13mm	7-13mm	7-13mm	7-13mm	7-13mm

Full designations and manufacturers are as follows:
Car, Half-Track, M-2 (Autocar Company, White Motor Company);
Carrier, Personnel, Half-Track, M-3 and M-3A1 (Autocar Company, Diamond T Motor Company, White Motor Company);
Carrier, 81mm Mortar, Half-Track, M-4A1 (White Motor Company);
Carrier, Half-Track, M-9A1 (International Harvester Company);

Half-Track of Israeli Army

Carriage, Motor, Multiple Gun, M-16 (White Motor Company).

Development/Variants
The United States developed half-track vehicles in the 1930s and they were produced in large numbers by various manufacturers during World War II. The above listing is only a selection of those that may be found in service. The dimensions vary on whether the vehicle has a winch or roller mounted at the front, whether a 12.7mm machine gun is fitted and whether racks are fitted on the sides of the vehicle. Many local modifications are in service; refer also to the section on Israel.

Employment

Half-Tracks are still used by Argentina, Austria (including M-3 and M-21 (81mm mortar)), Belgium, Brazil, Colombia, Cuba, Dominican Republic, Greece (and M16), Israel, Guatemala, Italy, Japan (M-15 and M-16), Mexico, Morocco, Portugal, Philippines, Spain (including M-16), Taiwan, Thailand (including M-16), Turkey, Uruguay, Venezuela (M-2 and M-9), Yugoslavia.

CAR, Scout, 4 x 4, M–3A1 — United States

This was manufactured by the White Motor Company. It is a 4 x 4 vehicle and was used as a radio vehicle, command vehicle, troop carrier and reconnaissance vehicle. Its basic data is as follows:

Length: 5.625m
Width: 2.032m
Height: 1.993m
Weight: 5920kg (loaded)
Armament: 1 x 12.7mm and 1 x 7.62mm machine guns
Engine: Hercules JXD developing 87hp at 2400rpm
Speed: 90km/ph (road)
Range: 410km
Fording: .71m
Gradient: 60%
Employment
Still in service with Brazil, Cambodia, Chile, Congo, Greece, Laos, Liberia, Mexico, Nicaragua, Peru, Vietnam, Thailand, Turkey, Yugoslavia.

LVTP–7 Amphibious Assault Vehicle — United States

Armament: 1 x 12.7mm M-85 machine gun elevation + 60°, depression − 15° 1000 rounds of ammunition
Crew: 3 + 25
Length: 7.94m
Width: 3.27m
Height: 3.26m (O/A)
3.12m (turret)
G/Clearance: .406m
Weight: 23,655kg (loaded)
18,257kg (empty)
G/Pressure: .576kg.cm^2
Engine: Detroit diesel model 8V53T, 8 cylinder, developing 400hp at 2800rpm
Speed: 64.37km/ph (road)
13.5km/ph (water)
Range: 482km (land)
Fuel: 681 litres
Fording: Amphibious
V/Obstacle: .914m
Trench: 2.438m
Gradient: 70%
Armour: 10mm–45mm

Development
The first prototype was completed in October 1967 and was known as the LVTPX-12. A total of 15 prototypes were built by July 1968. These vehicles were armed with a 20mm cannon. Development and production of the vehicle was undertaken by FMC under the supervision of the Naval Ships Systems Command. A production order for the LVTP-7 was given to FMC in June 1970 and the first vehicle was delivered to the USMC on 26th August 1971; production is now complete.

LVTP-7 of USMC

The LVTP-7 is fully amphibious being propelled in the water by two waterjets. It is constructed of welded aluminium armour. It has torsion bar and tube suspension and is fitted with infra-red driving lights.

Variants
LVTC-7: Landing Vehicle Tracked, Command Model 7. Prototype built in 1968 as LVTCX-2. It is a command vehicle and has a crew of 13. It carries additional radios and has an auxiliary power unit. A shelter can be erected if required.
LVTR-7: Landing Vehicle Tracked, Recovery Model 7. Prototype built in 1968 as the LVTRX-2. It has a winch, crane, welding equipment, pump, compressor, tools, etc.
LVTE-7: Landing Vehicle Tracked, Mine Clearing Model 7. Prototype built in 1970 as the LVTRX-3. Developed to clear paths through minefields. Not placed in production and no further development.
LVTHX-5: This was to have been a gun support vehicle, but did not enter production.

Employment
The LVTP-7 has replaced the LVTP-5 series in the United States Marine Corps and is also in service with Argentina, Italy, Spain and Thailand.

M–107 and M–110 Self-Propelled Guns   United States

	M-107	M-110
Crew:	5	5
Length in Travelling Order:	11.256m	7.457m
Length Hull W/O Spade:	5.72m	5.72m
Width:	3.149m	3.149m
Height (Top of Mount):	2.809m	2.809m
Height (Top of Barrel-Travelling):	3.679m	2.93m
G/Clearance:	.466m	.44m
Weight Loaded:	28,168kg	26,534kg
Weight Empty:	25,945kg	24,312kg
G/Pressure:	.81kg.cm²	.76kg.cm²
Speed Road:	56km/ph	56km/ph
Range Cruising:	725km	725km
Fuel:	1137 litres	1137 litres
Fording:	1.066m	1.066m
V/Obstacle:	1.016m	1.016m
Trench:	2.362m	2.362m
Gradient:	60%	60%
Main Armament Calibre:	175mm	203mm
Main Armament Designation:	M-113	M-2A1
Mount Designation:	M-158	M-158
A/A Armament:	—	—
Ammunition Carried:	2	2
Engine:	see below	see below

Development
Both of these weapons use a standard chassis designed by the Pacific Car and Foundry Company. The chassis is used for the M-107, M-110 and the M-578 ARV. This chassis was also used for the now discontinued T-119 and T-121 ARVs, 155mm T-245 SPG; parts were also used in the MICV-70 (XM-701). The M-107 and M-110 each have a total crew of 13 men, five are carried on the gun (driver in the front and two men either side of the gun), and the other eight in an M-548 support vehicle. This vehicle also carries the ammunition. The British Army uses the 6 × 6 Stalwart for this role. The M-107 and M-110 use the same engine, transmission and final drive as the M-108 and M-109.

The vehicles do not have anti-aircraft guns and the driver is the only member of the crew under cover. The British and American Armies have experimented with various covers to provide the crew with some protection against the weather and NBC warfare.

Variants
M-107: Design dates from 1957 and first prototype completed in February 1958 as the T-235; this became the T-235E1. The first production M-107 was completed in August 1962, the first unit was equipped at Fort Sill, Oklahoma, in January 1963. Manufacturers of the chassis have included FMC, Bowen-McLaughlin-York and Pacific Car and Foundry. The gun, which is made by Watervliet Arsenal, New York, has a

traverse of 30° left and 30° right, elevation being +65° and depression −2°. It is powered by a General Motors 8V71T 8 cylinder, liquid-cooled diesel developing 405hp at 2300rpm. The gun has a maximum range of 32,600m and fires an HE or chemical round.

M-110: Prototype was designated T-236 and later T-236E1, production dates, manufacturers and engine data is similar to the M-107. The 203mm (8in) howitzer has an elevation of +65° and a depression of −2°, traverse being 30° left and 30° right. Maximum range is 16,800m and it can fire nuclear or conventional shells.

M-110A1: Development started in December 1969 as the M-110E2 and this weapon is scheduled to replace both the M-107 and M-110 in a few years time. It has a longer barrel than the standard M-110 and fires HE, incendiary, nuclear, improved conventional munitions and dual purpose rounds. Range of the weapon has not been released. The loaded weight of the gun is 28,350kg and an overall length 10.261m.

Employment

M-107: Germany, Great Britain, Greece, Iran, Israel, Italy, Netherlands, Vietnam, Spain, United States (Army and Marines).
M-110: Belgium, Germany, Great Britain, Turkey, Iran, Israel, Netherlands, South Korea, United States, and Greece.

An M-110 Eight inch Howitzer of the British Army

M-107 of the British Army in Germany

M-110E1 guns whilst being tested in the USA

M55 Self-Propelled Howitzer   United States

Armament: 1 × 203mm M47 howitzer with an elevation of +65° and a depression of −5°
1 × .50 (12.7mm) Browning anti-aircraft machine gun
10 rounds of 203mm ammunition
900 rounds of .50 (12.7mm) ammunition
Crew: 6
Length: 7.908m
Width: 3.58m
Height: 3.469m (top of cupola)
3.124m (top of turret)
G/Clearance: .469m
Weight: 44,452kg (loaded)
30,823kg (empty)
G/Pressure: .78kg/cm²
Engine: Continental Model AV-1790-5B, 5C or 5D, 12 cylinder air-cooled petrol developing 704bhp at 2800rpm

Speed: 48km/hr
Range: 257km
Fuel: 1438 litres
Fording: 1.219m
V/Obstacle: 1.016m
Trench: 2.26m
Gradient: 60%
Armour: 13–26mm

Development
In 1948 The Pacific Car and Foundry Company started work on a series of self-propelled weapons. Two models were

Below: *Left to right—155mm M44, 155mm M53 and 8in M55 self-propelled artillery in action*

designed and built; these both used the same chassis and turret. They were the T97 (later to become the M53) and the T108 (later to become the M55). The prototypes were completed in 1952, followed by production vehicles in 1953. (The M53 is no longer in service with any country.) The engine and transmission is at the front of the vehicle with the turret at the rear. The latter has a traverse of 30° left and 30° right and all of the crew are seated in the turret including the driver. When in action a large spade is lowered down at the rear of the hull. The M55 fires a separate loading HE round to a maximum range of 16,916m. The full designation of the vehicle is Howitzer, Heavy, Self-Propelled: Full Tracked, 8-inch, M55. It was replaced in United States Army service by the M110 203mm (8-inch) self-propelled howitzer. The M55 is not provided with a NBC system and has no amphibious capability.

Variants
There are no variants of the M55 in service.

Employment
In service with Belgium and Italy.

M–108 & M–109
Self-Propelled Howitzers

United States

	M-108	M-109
Crew:	7	6
Length Gun Forward:	6.114m	6.612m
Length Vehicle Only:	6.114m	6.256m
Width Overall:	3.295m	3.295m
Width Reducable to:	3.149m	3.149m
Height Inc. Machine Gun:	3.28m	3.28m
Height W/O Machine Gun:	3.048m	3.06m
G/Clearance:	.451m	.467m
Weight Loaded:	22,452kg	23,786kg
Weight Empty:	18,436kg	19,730kg
G/Pressure:	.71kg.cm²	.766kg.cm²
Speed Road:	56km/ph	56km/ph
Speed Water:	6.43km/ph	6.43km/ph
Range Cruising:	360km	360km
Fuel:	511 litres	511 litres
Fording:	1.828m	1.828m
V/Obstacle:	.53m	.53m
Trench:	1.828m	1.828m
Gradient:	60%	60%
Main Armament Calibre:	105mm	155mm
Main Armament Designation:	M-103	M-126
Anti-Aircraft Gun:	12.7mm	12.7mm
Ammunition (Main) Rounds:	87	28
Ammunition (A/A) Rounds:	500	500
Engine:	both are powered by a Detroit Diesel Model 8V71T turbo-charged engine developing 405hp at 2300rpm	

Development/Variants
M-108: Development of the 110mm T-195 self-propelled howitzer commenced in 1953 and in 1956 it was decided to mount a 105mm weapon in place of the 110mm weapon. In 1959 designation was changed from T-195 to T-195E1, which became the M-108 in 1961. Production started in October 1962 and finished in September 1963, being produced by the GMC. Its 105mm gun can be elevated from −4° to +74°, turret traverse being 360°. Amphibious capabilities are the same as those of the M-109.

M-109: Development designations were T-196 and later T-196E1. The first prototype was built in 1961 followed by the first production vehicle in November 1962. The vehicle was built by the Allison Division of the General Motors Corporation at the Cleveland Tank-Automotive Plant. By 1976 2600 M-109s had been built. The turret has a traverse of 360°, elevation being +75° and depression −3°. The 155mm gun has a range of 14,700m and can fire three rounds a minute; it has a nuclear capability. Full designation is Howitzer, Medium, Self-Propelled M-109.

Right: *M-109U of Swiss Army*

Below: *M-108 of the Belgian Army*

The flotation equipment consists of nine air bags which are positioned four each side and one at the front of the vehicle, they are inflated in less than two minutes. The tracks propel the vehicle whilst in the water.

M-109A1: Development designation M-109E1. This version has a barrel 1.549m longer than that fitted to the M-109. This gives the weapon a range of 18,000m. Development started in 1967 and conversion of M-109s started in 1972 at depot maintenance level. All M-109s will be converted. This will also fire the Cannon Launched Guided Projectile.

M-109G: This is a German model of the M-109. Its differences are that it has a horizontal sliding breech-block by Rheinmetall (American M-109s have an interrupted screw breech-block), German aiming equipment. Range is 18,500m.

M-109U: This is the designation given to the model used by the Swiss Army. It has a semi-automatic loader of Swiss design. Rate of fire is 6 rounds a minute.

M-109 (Italy): The M-109s used by Italy have their armament built by Oto Melara. They have also developed and tested a model of the M-109 that has a new long barrel and fires rounds designed for the SP70. This has a range of 22,000m or 24,000m with SP70 shells.

Employment
M-108: Belgium, Brazil, Spain, United States.
M-109: Austria, Belgium, Canada, Denmark, Ethiopia, Germany, Great Britain, Iran, Israel, Italy, Libya (from Italy), Netherlands (they also have some without turrets used for driver training), Norway, Spain, Switzerland, United States.
XM-179: 155mm Self-Propelled Howitzer has been cancelled.

Above: *M-109A1 of the US Army*

M–44 and M–52 Self-Propelled Howitzers United States

	M-52	M-44	M-44A1
Crew:	5	5	5
Length Overall:	5.80m	6.159m	6.159m
Width:	3.149m	3.238m	3.238m
Height Inc. A/A MG:	3.31m	—	—
Height W/O A/A MG:	3.056m	—	—
Height with Canvas Cover:	—	3.11m	3.11m
G/Clearance:	.49m	.48m	.48m
Weight Loaded:	24,040kg	28,349kg	29,030kg
Weight Empty:	22,588kg	26,308kg	26,980kg
G/Pressure:	.60kg.cm^2	.66kg.cm^2	.67kg.cm^2
Speed Road:	56km/ph	56km/ph	56km/ph
Range Cruising:	160km	122km	122km
Fuel:	678 litres	568 litres	568 litres
Fording:	1.219m	1.066m	1.066m
V/Obstacle:	.914m	.762m	.762m
Trench:	1.828m	1.828m	1.828m
Gradient:	60%	60%	60%
Main Armament Calibre:	105mm	155mm	155mm
A/A Armament Calibre:	12.7mm	12.7mm	12.7mm
Ammunition (Main) Rounds:	105	24	24
Ammunition (A/A) Rounds:	900	900	900
Armour:	20mm (max)	20mm (max)	20mm (max)
Engine:	see below	see below	see below

Development/Variants

General: Both the M-44 and M-52 use many components of the M-41 light tank, including the engine, transmission and auxilliary engine. The M-44 and M-52 have similar chassis. Both have their engines and transmission at the front and the turret or the fighting compartment at the rear. All of the crew are in the rear of the vehicle.

M-44: Development started in 1947 as the T-99 and the first prototypes were built in 1950 at Detroit Arsenal. The next model was the T-99E1; in 1952 this was redesig-nated T-194. In 1953 it was standardised as the M-44. The M-44 is armed with a 155mm M-45 howitzer in a mount M-80, traverse being 30° left and 30° right, elevation being +65° and depres-sion −5°. The vehicle is powered by a Continental AOS-895-3 petrol engine developing 500hp at 2800rpm. The M-44A1 is similar to the M-44 but is powered by a Continental AOS1-895-5 petrol engine with a fuel injection system. There is no overhead armour protection for the crew of the M-44. A canvas cover can be erected over the fighting compartment if required. When in the firing position a spade is let down at the rear of the vehicle and the back of the fighting compartment folds down to provide a platform for the crew to operate the gun.

M-52: The first pilot model was designated the T-98 and armed with a 155mm howitzer. It was built at Detroit Arsenal in 1950. This was followed by the T-98E1 which was armed with a 105mm howitzer. This became the M-52. The M-52 is armed with an M-49 105mm howitzer in a mount M-85. The turret has a traverse of 60° left and 60° right. Elevation is +65° and

depression is −10°. The M-52 is powered by a 6 cylinder air-cooled petrol engine; this is a Continental AOS-895-3 developing 500hp at 2800rpm. The M-52A1 is powered by a Continental AOS1-895-5 with a fuel injection system fitted. This gives the vehicle a maximum speed of 68km/ph.

Employment
M-44: Greece, Italy, Japan, Jordan, Spain, Turkey.
M-52: Belgium (reserve), Greece, Japan, Jordan.

Left: *M-44 of the US Army*

Left: *M-52 105mm SPG*

Below: *M-44 of Japanese Self-Defence Force*

M–7 and M–7B1
Self-Propelled Howitzer

United States

Armament: 1 × 105mm howitzer, elevation + 35°, depression − 5°, traverse 30° left and 15° right of centre line
69 rounds of 105mm ammunition carried
1 × 12.7mm anti-aircraft machine gun and 300 rounds of ammunition
Crew: 7
Length: 6.02m (6.18m) (overall)
Width: 2.88m (2.93m)
Height: 2.946m (including machine gun)
G/Clearance: .43m (.44m)
Weight: 22,970kg (22,680kg) (loaded)
G/Pressure: .73kg.cm²
Engine: See below
Speed: 39km/ph (32km/ph)
Range: 137km (200km)
Fuel: 677 litres (636) litres
Fording: 1.22m (.91m)
V/Obstacle: .61m
Trench: 2.23m
Gradient: 60%
Armour: 12mm–62mm

Note. *The data in brackets relates to the M-7B1. Deep fording equipment could be fitted.*

Development
Development commenced in June 1941 as the T-32, pilots were built by the American Locomotive Company and it was standardised as the M-7 in February 1942. Production commenced in 1942. The

vehicle saw extensive service with Allied Forces from the battle of El Alamein onwards. It was given the name 'Priest'. The 105mm howitzer had a range of 11,160m.

Variants
M-7: This was based on the M-4 chassis and manufactured by the American Locomotive Company. Powered by a Continental Model R-975-C1, 9 cylinder, radial petrol engine developing 350hp at 2400rpm.
M-7B1: This was based on the M-4A3 chassis and built by Pressed Steel Company. Powered by a Ford GAA V8 engine developing 450hp at 2600rpm. It was standardised in September 1942.
M-7B2: Very few of these were built by Federal Machine and Welder Company.

Employment
Used by Belgium, Brazil, Israel, Italy, Jordan, Pakistan, Portugal, Turkey, Yugoslavia.

M-7 105mm Self-Propelled Howitzer

M–56 Scorpion
Self-Propelled Anti-Tank Gun

Armament: 1 × 90mm gun M-54 in mount M-88 with 29 rounds of ammunition
Crew: 4
Length: 5.841m (including gun)
4.555m (excluding gun)
Width: 2.577m
Height: 2.057m
G/Clearance: .38m
Weight: 7030kg (loaded)
5783kg (empty)
G/Pressure: .316kg.cm²
Engine: Continental AO1-403-5, 6 cylinder, air-cooled, fuel injection petrol engine developing 200bhp at 3000rpm
Speed: 45km/ph (road)
Range: 225km (cruising)
Fuel: 208 litres
Fording: 1.066m (without kit)
1.524m (with kit)
V/Obstacle: .762m
Trench: 1.524m
Gradient: 60%
Armour: See below

Development
The M-56 uses many components of the M-76 amphibious carrier OTTER. The development designation of the M-56 was the T-101 and later T-101E1. The production contract was signed in 1950. The weapon was troop tested with the 101st Airborne Division in 1953. The M-56 was in service by 1957 and the last vehicle was completed in May 1959.

The Scorpion is armed with a 90mm gun that fires similar ammunition to the M-48 tank. The gun has a vertical sliding breech-block and has an elevation of +15° and a depression of −10°, traverse being 30° left and 30° right. The chassis of the M-56 is unarmoured and fabricated from sheeting and rolled sections of aluminium and is riveted and welded together. The only armour on the vehicle is the shield.

The vehicle has been replaced in the United States Army by the M-551 Sheridan. The M-56 was too light for the gun fitted and when the main armament was fired the vehicle moved several feet.

Variants
There are no variants in service although many versions were projected or built as prototypes including: missile carrier, anti-aircraft vehicle with 4 × 12.7mm machine guns, 81mm and 107mm mortar carriers, 106mm recoilless rifle carriers, amphibious armoured personnel carrier. One was also fitted with a gas turbine engine.

Employment
Used by Morocco and the Spanish Marines.

The M-56 Scorpion Self-Propelled Anti-Tank Weapon

M–10 and M–36

Self-Propelled Anti-Tank Gun

United States

	M-10	M-10A1	M-36	M-36B1	M-36B2
Crew:	5	5	5	5	5
Length:	5.97m	5.97m	5.97m	6.27m	5.97m
Width:	3.05m	3.05m	3.05m	2.55m	3.05m
Height:	2.47m	2.47m	3.19m	2.66m	3.15m
G /Clearance:	.43m	.43m	.44m	.43m	.46m
Weight Loaded:	29,940kg	29,030kg	27,670kg	30,840kg	29,940kg
G /Pressure:	.86kg.cm^2	.86kg.cm^2	.95kg.cm^2	.96kg.cm^2	.67kg.cm^2
Speed Road:	48km /ph	48km /ph	42km /ph	42km /ph	40km /ph
Range Cruising:	320km	260km	180km	160km	180km
Fuel:	621 litres	727 litres	727 litres	636 litres	625 litres
Fording:	.91m	.91m	.91m	.91m	1.07m
V /Obstacle:	.61m	.61m	.46m	.61m	.48m
Trench:	2.29m	2.29m	2.29m	2.29m	2.29m
Gradient:	60%	60%	60%	60%	60%
Main Armament:	76.2mm	76.2mm	90mm	90mm	90mm
Bow Armament:	—	—	—	7.62mm	—
A /A Armament:	12.7mm	12.7mm	12.7mm	12.7mm	12.7mm
Ammun. Main:	54	54	47	47	47
Ammun. 7.62mm:	—	—	—	450	—
Ammun. 12.7mm:	300	300	1000	1000	1000
Engine:	GM(2)	Ford GAA	Ford GAA	Ford GAA	GMC(2)
Bhp /rpm:	375 /2100	450 /2600	450 /2600	450 /2600	375 /2100
Armour:	12mm-50mm	12mm-50mm	12mm-50mm	12mm-50mm	12mm-50mm

Development /Variants

The above tank destroyers were developed during World War II and saw service in Europe from 1943 onwards. The M-10, M-10A1, M-36 and M-36B2 all incorporate a Sherman chassis with a new hull and turret. The M-36B1 retains the chassis and hull (and its bow machine gun) of the M-4A3, and is fitted with a new turret and gun. The M-36 uses an M-10A1 chassis and the M36B2 the M-10 chassis. A prime mover version of the M-10 was called the M-35. The British converted many M-10s and M-10A1s to carry the excellent 17 Pounder gun. These were called 17 Pounder Self-Propelled Achilles.

Employment

M-10s are still used by Denmark (Achilles) and South Korea.

M-36s are still used by Pakistan (M-36B2), South Korea, Turkey, Yugoslavia (M-36B2).

M-10 Tank Destroyer, at Aberdeen Proving Ground Museum.

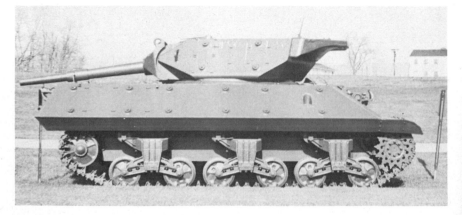

M–18 Self-Propelled Anti-Tank Gun United States

Armament: 1 × 76mm M-1A1 or M-1A2 gun, elevation + 19½°, depression − 10°
1 × 12.7mm anti-aircraft machine gun
45 rounds of 76mm ammunition
1000 rounds of 12.7mm ammunition
Crew: 5
Length: 6.654m (including gun)
5.282m (excluding gun)
Width: 2.87m (see note)
Height: 2.57m (including A/A machine gun)
G/Clearance: .355m
Weight: 17,650kg (loaded)
16,120kg (empty)
G/Pressure: .83kg.cm²
Engine: Continental R-975-C4, 9 cylinder, radial petrol engine developing 400hp at 2400rpm OR Continental R-975-C1 developing 350hp at 2400rpm
Speed: 88.5km/ph (road)
Range: 240km (cruising)
Fuel: 625 litres
Fording: 1.22m
V/Obstacle: .914m
Trench: 1.879m
Gradient: 60%
Armour: 7mm–25mm

Note. *The width of the vehicle depends on the tracks fitted.*

Development/Variants
The M-18 was developed during World

War II and its development designation was T-70. It was standardised as the M-18 in February 1944. A total of 2507 were built by October 1944 when production was completed. Production was undertaken by the Buick Motor Division of the General Motors Corporation.
The M-18 was often called the Hellcat. Its primary role was of tank hunting and the vehicle relied on its high speed to get itself out of trouble, its armour being very thin.
There were a number of variants on the M-18 chassis including the M-39 and M-44 armoured utility vehicles, none of which are known to remain in service. In addition there were many experimental vehicles.

Employment
Used by Greece, Nationalist China, South Korea, Venezuela and Yugoslavia.

Above: *M-18 Hellcat*

181

M–42

Self-Propelled Anti-Aircraft Gun System

Armament: 2 x 40mm cannon M-2A1 with 480 rounds of ammunition
1 x M-1919A4 7.62mm machine gun with 1750 rounds
Crew: 6
Length: 6.356m (including guns)
5.819m (excluding guns)
Width: 3.225m
Height: 2.847m
G /Clearance: .438m
Weight: 22,452kg (loaded)
G /Pressure: .65kg.cm²
Engine: M-42 has Continental or Lycoming AOS-895-3, M-42A1 has a Continental or Lycoming AOS1-895-5, 6 cylinder air-cooled, supercharged petrol engine developing 500hp at 2800rpm
Speed: 72km /ph (road)
Range: 161km (cruising)
Fuel: 530 litres
Fording: 1.016m
V /Obstacle: .711m
Trench: 1.828m
Gradient: 60%
Armour: 10mm–32mm

Development /Variants

The development designation was T-141 and the prototype was built at Cleveland, Ohio. The first production M-42 was completed in 1952 and production continued until 1957 after 3700 had been built. It uses many of the components of the M-41 light tank family.

The 40mm cannon are mounted in a power-operated turret and have a traverse of 360°, powered elevation is from −3°

to +85°, or from −5° to +87° manually. The guns have a cyclic rate of fire of 240 rounds per minute and a maximum effective range of 4700m.

The M-42A1 has a fuel injection system fitted to its engine. This increases the power of the engine to 525bhp as well as a small extension in its operating range.

In the 1950s an M-42 was fitted with a radar system on the right side of the guns; this however did not enter production.

The crew of six are seated four in the turret and two in the front of the vehicle.

Employment

Used by Austria, Germany, Japan, Jordan, Lebanon, Vietnam and the United States.

M-42 of the US Army

M–88

Armoured Recovery Vehicle (Medium)

Armament: 1 x 12.7mm machine gun M-2
1500 rounds of 12.7mm ammunition
Crew: 4
Length: 8.254m (including blade)
Width: 3.428m
Height: 3.22m (including machine gun)
2.921m (excluding machine gun)
G/Clearance: .457m
Weight: 50,800kg (loaded)
G/Pressure: .74kg.cm^2
Engine: Continental AVS1-1790-6A, 12 cylinder, air-cooled, supercharged petrol engine developing 980bhp at 2800rpm
Speed: 48km/ph (road)
Range: 360km
Fuel: 1685 litres
Fording: 1.625m
V/Obstacle: 1.066m
Trench: 2.616m
Gradient: 60%

Development/Variants
Design of the M-88 (development designation T-88) commenced in 1954. The vehicle is based on components of the M-48 tank series. By February 1959, three prototypes had been built and these were found to be satisfactory.
Production of the M-88 was undertaken by Bowen-McLaughlin-York Incorporated at their Bair facility. The first production M-88 was completed in 1961, the first order being for 498 vehicles. Production continued until 1964 by which time about 1000 had been built.
A hydraulically operated dozer blade is mounted on the front of the vehicle. This can be used for dozing operations or for supporting the vehicle when the boom is being used. The boom has a capacity of 6078kg without the support of the dozer blade, and 25,400kg with the use of the dozer blade.
The main winch has 60.96m of cable and a maximum pull of 40,823kg at 8.3m per minute. The hoist winch has 121.9m of cable and a maximum capacity of 22,680kg (bare drum low speed). The winch and hoist are hydraulically operated.
The M-88, when built, had a cupola-mounted 12.7mm machine gun. Most have had these removed and replaced by an unprotected machine gun mount.
Trials have been carried out with deep fording equipment. This has not however been adopted for service.
In 1973 trials were under way with an M-88E1. This has many components of the M-60 series, including a diesel engine and a diesel auxiliary power unit. It was announced in 1976 that the vehicle was to be placed in production again and that a conversion programme would be started to update M-88's to M-88A1 standard. These will have numerous improvements including a diesel engine.

Employment
In service with Austria, Israel, Germany, Norway, Greece, Pakistan, and United States Army.

Rear view of an M-88 Armoured Recovery Vehicle

M–578
Light Armoured Recovery Vehicle

Armament: 1 × 12.7mm machine gun M-2
500 rounds of 12.7mm machine gun ammunition
Crew: 3
Length: 6.42m (including crane)
5.937m (hull only)
Width: 3.149m
Height: 2.921m (without machine gun)
G/Clearance: .47m
Weight: 24,470kg
G/Pressure: .71kg.cm² (loaded)
Engine: GMC 8V71T Detroit diesel, liquid-cooled, 8 cylinder, turbo-charged, developing 425hp at 1700rpm
Speed: 59.5km/ph (road)
Range: 725km (cruising)
Fuel: 1137 litres
Fording: 1.066m
V/Obstacle: 1.016m
Trench: 2.362m
Gradient: 60%

Development/Variants
The M-578 (development designation T-120 and later T-120E1) uses the same chassis as the M-107 and M-110 self-propelled guns. The first production M-578 was completed by FMC Corporation in October 1962. Later the vehicle was manufactured by Bowen-Mclaughlin-York Incorporated and the Pacific Car and Foundry Company. Other trials versions were the T-119 and the T-121.

The vehicle has a hoisting capacity of 13,620kg, with the crane turret traversed to the rear and the spade in position. The tow winch has 70.10m of .03m cable with the following capacities:
Bare drum, 27,240kg, 610 metres/minute, low gear.
Bare drum, 6724kg, 24.38 metres/minute, high gear.
Full drum, 17,343kg, 14.33 metres/minute, low gear.
Full drum, 4290kg, 58.52 metres/minute, high gear.
The turret has a traverse of 360°. The hoist/winch capacity is the following (76.20m of .002m cable):
Bare drum, 6810kg, 9.14 metres/minute, low gear.
Bare drum, 1553kg, 40.23 metres/minute, high gear.
Full drum, 4159kg, 14.94 metres/minute, low gear.
Full drum, 944kg, 65.84 metres/minute, high gear.
A wheel lockout system transmits lifting forces directly to the ground.

Employment
In service with Brazil, Canada, Denmark, Great Britain, Netherlands, Norway, Spain and the United States.

An M-578 Armoured Recovery Vehicle of the Danish Army

M–980   Yugoslavia
Mechanised Infantry Combat Vehicle

Armament: 1 × 20mm cannon with an elevation of + 80° and a depression of − 5°
1 × 7.92mm co-axial MG
2 × launchers for Sagger ATGWS.
Crew: 3 + 6–8
Length: 6.25m
Width: 2.85m
Height: 2.16m (turret)
1.73m (hull roof)
Weight: 12,000kg (loaded)
10,500kg (empty)
Engine: HS 115-2 V-8 turbo-charged diesel developing 276hp at 3000rpm
Speed: 70km/hr
8km/hr (water)
Range: 500km
Fording: Amphibious
V/Obstacle: 1m
Trench: 2.4m
Gradient: 60%

Note. *The above data is provisional.*

Development
The Yugoslav M-980 was first displayed at the 1975 May Day Parade in Belgrade and it has now started to supplement the older M-60 armoured personnel carrier. The M-980 uses some components of the French AMX-10P MICV including the

engine and also possibly the suspension.
The engine is at the front of the hull with the driver on the left side and the commander to the rear of the driver. The turret is in the centre of the hull with the personnel compartment at the rear. The 20mm cannon is the Model M-55, this being the Swiss Hispano Suiza Type 804 cannon which has been manufactured in Yugoslavia for some years. The 7.92mm M-53 machine gun is mounted to the right of the main armament, the M-53 is the German MG-42 built in Yugoslavia. The infantry is provided with firing ports and vision devices in the sides and rear of the hull which enable the crew to fire their weapons from within the hull.
The M-980 is provided with a NBC system and a full range of night vision equipment. It is fully amphibious being propelled in the water by its tracks, before entering the water a trim vane is erected at the front of the hull.
Variants
There are no known variants of the M-980.
Employment
In service with the Yugoslav Army.

Above: *The Yugoslav M-980 Mechanised Infantry Combat Vehicle*

M60 Armoured Personnel Carrier   Yugoslavia

Armament: 1 × 12.7mm machine gun on roof
1 × 7.92mm machine gun in bow
Crew: 3 + 10
Length: 5.05m
Width: 2.75m
Height: 1.8m (w/o armament)
Weight Loaded: 9500kg
G/Pressure: .6kg/cm²

Engine: FAMOS 6 cylinder in-line water-cooled diesel developing 140hp
Speed: 45km/hr
6km/hr (water)
Range: 400km
Fuel: 130 litres
Fording: Amphibious
V/Obstacle: .6m
Trench: 2m

Gradient: 60%
Armour: 10–25mm

Development

The M-60 (it has previously been known in the West as the M-1965 or the M-590) entered service with the Yugoslav Army in the early 1960s. The vehicle uses the suspension and tracks of the Russian 76mm SU-76 self-propelled gun. The M-60 is fully amphibious being propelled in the water by its tracks, a trim vane is erected at the front of the hull before it enters the water.

The main armament consists of a Browning 12.7mm machine gun mounted on the roof, there is also a 7.92mm M-53

machine gun mounted on the hull front firing forwards. The M-53 is the Yugoslav version of the German MG42 weapon of the Second World War. The personnel compartment at the rear of the hull is provided with firing ports in the sides and rear. The vehicle is not fitted with a NBC system and has no night vision equipment.

Variants

There are no known variants of the M-60 APC.

Employment

In service in Cyprus and with the Yugoslav Army.

Above: *Infantry dismount from their M-60 APC*

SK–1 Armoured Car

Armament: 1 × 7.92mm MG 34
Crew: 5
Length: 4.00m
Width: 2.00m
Height: 2.80m
G/Clearance: .28m
Weight: 5400kg (loaded)
Engine: Model 30K, 4 cylinder, in-line, petrol engine developing 55hp at 2800rpm
Speed: 80km/ph (road)
Range: 350km
Fording: .54m
V/Obstacle: .40m
Track: 1.50m

Egypt

Egypt has built a number of 4 × 4 armoured personnel carriers called the WALID. This is very similar in appearance to the Soviet BTR-40 vehicle and is powered by an air-cooled German Deutz engine. They are in service with Algeria, Egypt, Israel and the Yemen. Egypt did have a number of Sherman tanks fitted with AMX-13 turrets.

East Germany

Wheelbase: 3.77m
Armour: 8mm

The SK-1 entered service in 1954; it is not used by the East German Army but is used by para-military units. The vehicle is based on the East German Robur Garant 30K 4 × 4 truck. The SK-1 is very similar in appearance to the Soviet BA-64 armoured car. The East German SK-2 is a six-wheeled armoured water cannon. The East Germans have modified T-34s and SU-76s to their own requirements. Refer to their respective sections for full details.

As far as is known none of these remain in service; they have either been destroyed in combat or captured by Israel.

India

India builds the Vickers MBT Mk 1 in a new tank factory near Madras. For full details of the Vickers MBT and the Indian production of the tank refer to the page on the Vickers MBT Mk 1.

Italy

Oto Melara S.p.A. of La Spezia have built 200 M-60A1 tanks for the Italian Army and over 4000 M-113 APCs for the Italian, Libyan and Turkish Armies. They have recently modified a M113A1 to fulfil MICV role (e.g. similar to FMC AIFV). They have also fitted the main armament to M-109s supplied by the United States. M-109s have been supplied by Oto Melara to Italy and Libya. Oto Melara has overhauled many M-47s to overseas countries. Refer to M-47 page for details of the M-47 rebuilt by Oto Melara. Oto Melara are building 600 Leopard tanks for the Italian Army. There is a separate page for the new Fiat wheeled armoured vehicles.

Romania

The Romanians have built an armoured personnel carrier known as the TAB-70. This is now in service in some numbers and is believed to be based on the Russian BTR-60 armoured personnel carrier.

South Africa

South Africa has built over 1000 AML armoured cars under licence from Panhard, although some components are still imported from France; this is known as the Eland. Some Panhards have been supplied by South Africa to Rhodesia. South Africa also has in service the Cactus surface-to-air missile system; this is called Crotale by the French. The South Africans paid for the initial development of the system. In 1969 it was reported that South Africa was testing two heavy tanks. Since then nothing more has been reported and these could well have been Israeli tanks under test. More recently it was reported that South Africa was testing a new light tank.

Some World War II Marmon-Herrington Mk IV/F armoured cars are still used in Cyprus. They are armed with a two pounder gun and a 7.62mm machine gun.

Spain

The Pegaso Company of Madrid has developed a 6 x 6 armoured personnel carrier. This is reported to have a hull of welded aluminium construction and to be fitted with a hydropneumatic suspension system and a NBC system. No further information is available at the present time. For some time Spain has been assembling AMX-30 tanks and has recently started a major refit and modernisation programme for her fleet of M47 tanks.

Turkey

Turkey is to establish facilities for the construction of armoured vehicles, and the first AFVs to be built will be the Leopard MBT.

New Light Tank   Germany

The German Army has a requirement for a new light tank weighing less than ten tons. This is still in the design stage; a prototype has yet to be built.

Mechanised Infantry Combat Vehicle Great Britain

A Mechanised Infantry Combat Vehicle is being developed to replace the current FV432 armoured personnel carrier.

SP–70 International

The SP-70 is a joint development by Germany, Great Britain and Italy to develop a Self-Propelled 155mm weapon using the ordnance of the FH-70 suitably modified. Great Britain is responsible for the turret and Germany for the chassis.

SP-70 is scheduled to enter service in 1985. As of late 1976 the prototype was not completed. It is being built in Germany and uses some components of the Leopard 1 Main Battle Tank.

New Light Tank United States

The United States has started design work on a new light tank. No further details of this project are available although it would appear that it will be heavier than the German light tank. There is a possibility that Germany and the United States will co-operate together to design a new light tank.

Other Armoured Fighting Vehicles

CATI	Tank Destroyer	Belgium	No longer in service
Chrysler SWAT	APC	United States	Development cancelled
Conqueror	Heavy Tank	Great Britain	No longer in service
Cutia-Vete	Reconnaissance	Brazil	Still used by Brazil
G-13	Tank Destroyer	Germany /Swiss	No longer in service
Hornet Malkara	ATGW Vehicle	Great Britain	No longer in service
Hotchkiss LFU	Light AFV	France	Development cancelled
Hotchkiss TT A 12	APC	France	Development cancelled
HWR 42	Armoured Car	Germany	Development cancelled
IKV-102/103	Tank Destroyer	Sweden	Being phased out
LVT-4	APC (Amphibious)	USA	Taiwan may still have a few in sevice
LVPT-5	APC (Amphibious)	USA	No longer in service
M2, M-4, M-6,M-8	APC /Armoured Car	France	Development cancelled
M-39	Utility Vehicle	United States	No longer in service
M-50 (Ontos)	Tank Destroyer	United States	No longer in service
M-51	Heavy ARV	United States	No longer in service
M-53	SPG	United States	No longer in service
M-103	Heavy Tank	United States	No longer in service
MBT-70	MBT	FRG /USA	Development cancelled
MOWAG PUMA	APC	Switzerland	Development cancelled
m /43	SPG	Sweden	Being phased out
Pbv. 301	APC	Sweden	No longer in service
Strv. 74	Light Tank	Sweden	No longer in service
Strv. 40	Light Tank	Sweden	Dominica may still have a few
SKP /VKP m /42	APC	Sweden	Still used by the Swedish Army
VEAK 40	SPAAG	Sweden	Development cancelled
XM 701	MICV	United States	Development cancelled
XM 729	RAMS (for Vietnam)	United States	Development cancelled
XM 733	RAMS (for Vietnam)	United States	Development cancelled
XM 800	Reconnaissance	United States	Development cancelled
XM 803	MBT	United States	Development cancelled
XM 808 (Twister)	Reconnaissance	United States	Development cancelled
YP-104	Reconnaissance	Netherlands	Development cancelled

Glaads

United States

The United States Army has a requirement to replace the current clear weather 20mm Vulcan Air Defence System. Philco-Ford have mounted twin 25mm cannon on a modified MICV (XM701) chassis and started firing trials early in 1976. Also being studied is the possibility of mounting the 30mm General Electric cannon, as used on the A-10 Attack Aircraft, onto a M-109 chassis. Other contenders are believed to be the German Gepard (which has been tested in the United States) and a modified Bofors 40mm gun on a self-propelled chassis.

Photo Credits

The photographs used to illustrate this book have been received from many Governments, companies and individuals all over the world. The sources, where known, are listed below.

Alvis Company (Great Britain) 68 (Foot), 69 (Top)
Associated Press (Great Britain) 103
Austrian Army 8, 142 (Top), 148 (Foot)
Bell, T 65 (Lower)
Berliet Company (France) 35 (Foot)
British Aircraft Corporation (Great Britain) 69 (Foot), 75 (Top), 166 (Cent)
British Ministry of Defence (ARMY) 59, 60, 61, 70 (Top), 72, 74, 75 (Foot), 76, 79, 80, 81, 172
Bundesgrenzshutz 138
Cadillac Gage Company (USA) 158, 159
Creusot—Loire Company (France) 39
DAF Company (The Netherlands) 2, 3, 95
E.C.P. Armées (France) 19 (Top and Foot), 21, 24, 29, 37, 38 (Foot), 40
Egyptian Ministry of Defence 15, 109
Electronique Marcel Dassault (France) 34
Engesa Company (Brazil) 10, 11
Euromissile (France/Germany) 20 (Foot), 30 (Foot)
Fiat Company (Italy) 88, 89
FMC Corporation (USA) 154, 161, 162, 164 (Centre and Foot), 165, 166 (Top and Foot)
F.N. (Belgium) 9
Foss, Christopher F 23, 30 (Top), 32 (Foot), 35 (Top), 70 (Foot), 178, 180
GKN Sankey (Great Britain) 78
German Army 38 (Top), 57 (Foot), 58
GIAT (France) 20 (Top and Centre)
Hägglund and Söner (Sweden) 126, 130, 131
Israel Aircraft Industries (Israel) 84
Japanese Self Defence Force 92, 93
Krauss Maffei (Germany) 44, 46, 47 (Top)
Ledford, M 97
LOHR Company (France) 28

Mak Maschinenbau Company (Germany) 47 (Centre and Foot)
Mitsubishi Heavy Industries (Japan) 90, 91
Messerschmitt—Bolkow—Blohm Company (Germany) 57 (Top)
MOWAG Company (Switzerland) 135, 136, 137
Panhard and Levassor (France) 25, 26, 27 (Top and Foot), 33, 34
Rauch, G Von 147
Rheinmetall Company (Germany) 55
Royal Armoured Corps Tank Museum (Great Britain) 67 (Top)
Royal Netherlands Army 22, 31, 32 (Top), 64, 156
SAMM Company (France) 27 (Centre)
Short Brothers and Harland (Great Britain) 73, 77
Soltam Company (Israel) 86, 87
Steyr—Daimler—Puch Company (Austria) 7
Swedish Ministry of Defence 125, 129
Swiss Ministry of Defence 65 (Top), 133, 134, 175 (Top)
Taibo, J I 148 (Top)
TASS 111
Technology Investments Company (Eire) 17
Thomson CSF (France) 42
Thyssen—Henschel (Germany) 48, 49, 50, 51, 52, 53, 54
Tunbridge, S 128, 175 (Foot), 184
Thune Company (Norway) 152
United States Army 140, 143, 146 (Foot), 147, 150, 155, 168, 169, 173, 176, 177 (Top and Centre), 179, 181, 182, 183
United States Marine Corps 170
Verganelakis, G 19 (Centre), 146 (Top)
Vickers Company (Great Britain) 63, 80
Yamada, S 94, 177 (Foot)

Index